fact
files

AMY-JANE BEER
and
PAT MORRIS

MAMMALS

CHARTWELL
BOOKS, INC.

Published by
# CHARTWELL BOOKS, INC.
A Division of **BOOK SALES, INC.**
114 Northfield Avenue
Edison, New Jersey 08837


The Brown Reference Group plc
8 Chapel Place
Rivington Street
London EC2A 3DQ
www.brownreference.com

© 2005 The Brown Reference Group plc.

ISBN 0-7858-1967-3

**Editorial Director:** Lindsey Lowe

**Project Director:** Graham Bateman

**Art Director:** Steve McCurdy

**Editors:** Derek Hall, Virginia Carter

**Artists:** Denys Ovenden, Priscilla Barrett, with Michael Long,
          Graham Allen, Malcolm McGregor

Printed in China

# Contents

# Introduction

**M**ammals are the most advanced form of life to appear on this planet to date. They evolved from inconspicuous mammal-like reptiles that existed some 200 million years ago, when the dinosaurs were in their ascendancy. The first true mammals looked like today's solenodons and fed on insects that they caught at night.

Today there are about 4,680 species of mammals alive. About one-third are rodents (rats, mice, squirrels, and so on). And one in five is a bat. The smallest mammal is Kitti's hog-nosed bat, *Craseonycteris thonglongyai*, which weighs only about one-twentieth of an ounce (1.5 g), while the largest is the blue whale, *Balaenoptera musculus*, which weighs up to 130 tonnes or more.

As well as vast differences in size, mammals have varied lifestyles. The naked mole rat, *Heterocephalus glaber*, stays in a single burrow for its entire life, while some whales and seals travel over 10,000 miles (16,000 km) on annual migrations. Some mammals live solitary lives except when they meet to mate; others form vast colonies numbering thousands. Yet others live permanently in tightly organized social systems in which each individual knows its place. Some defend territory with sophisticated scent-marking and recognition systems. Some mammals have only one young at a time, often at intervals well in excess of a year, but mice and rabbits breed almost continuously. Some mammals can run very fast, but there are also swimmers, burrowers, gliders, and flyers. Mammals range from the poles to the tropics and from oceans, lakes, and rivers to deserts. They eat grass, flesh, fish, insects, fruit, bamboo, nectar, and gum. They shout, sing, and stay silent. Mammals are truly the world's most diverse and adaptable group. The *Animal Fact File: Mammals* demonstrates this diversity.

## What Makes a Mammal?

Mammals are often described as "warm-blooded"; the more correct term is endothermic. Reptiles and even some fish are also warm inside, but they cannot maintain a high blood temperature without basking in the sun or constantly moving around to generate heat from their muscles—they are ectothermic. Mammals (like birds) differ in that they generate heat internally, so their temperature is not only high but is kept constant at 95 to 100°F (35–38°C), depending on the species. The scientific term for such animals is homeothermic.

Mammal bodies are covered in hair (sometimes very sparsely). Hair traps a layer of air next to the skin, which insulates it from extremes of temperature around it. Mammals also sweat and lose heat as the moisture evaporates. Mammals also have a variety of shapes and sizes of teeth to suit their different diets. They are not the only animals to bear live young, but they are unique in that mothers produce milk, which means that the infants have no need to forage for food.

## About this Book

Just by looking, we can see that lions, tigers, and the domestic cat are related, and that rats and mice are quite different from deer and antelope. Scientists take this study much further and to minute detail in the science of taxonomy, in which detailed relationships are worked out using a hierarchy of categories called taxa. Mammals all belong to the class Mammalia, which is divided into 27 orders. Examples include the order Carnivora (flesh-eating mammals such as lions, wolves, and otters) and Rodentia (rodents such as rats and mice). In the *Animal Fact File: Mammals* you will find representatives of most mammal orders, which are color coded and listed on pages 3 to 5. Within an order such as Carnivora, for example, all catlike mammals are placed in the same family (Felidae), and doglike mammals in the family Canidae. Very closely related cats such as the lion and the tiger are grouped in the genus *Panthera*. Lions are distinguished from, say, tigers by the scientific names *Panthera leo* and *Panthera tigris* respectively. In this book you will find illustrated articles on 244 species of mammals, grouped by order and family.

Each article follows a fixed structure. The color-coded header strip denotes the order to which each animal belongs and gives its common name. The fact panel then lists its scientific name and other taxonomic information followed by sections that describe different features of the animal and its lifestyle. Like all animals, the survival of many mammals is in doubt as they suffer from pressures brought to bear by humans. Under the heading "Status" information is given on the threats or lack of threat facing each animal. For definitions of the categories of threat see Glossary under IUCN and CITES. Finally, a world map visually portrays the distribution of each species, showing its natural range, unless indicated.

| Rank | Scientific name | Common name |
|---|---|---|
| Phylum | Chordata | Animals with a backbone |
| Class | Mammalia | All mammals |
| Order | Carnivora | Flesh-eaters/carnivores |
| Family | Felidae | All cats |
| Genus | *Panthera* | Big cats |
| Species | *leo* | Lion |

*The kingdom Animalia is subdivided into phylum, classes, orders, families, genera, and species. Above is the classification of the lion.*

# Lion

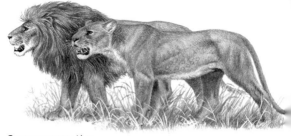

**Common name** Lion

**Scientific name** *Panthera leo*

**Family** Felidae

**Order** Carnivora

**Size** Length head/body: 5–8 ft (1.4–2.5 m); tail length: 27.5–41 in (70–105 cm); height at shoulder: 42–48 in (107–123 cm). Male 20–50% bigger than female

**Weight** 265–550 lb (120–250 kg)

**Key features** Huge, muscular cat with long, thin tail tipped with black tuft; body light buff to tawny brown; male develops thick mane of dark fur; head large with powerful, crushing jaws; eyes yellowish-brown

**Habits** Lives in prides; hunts alone and cooperatively; most active between dusk and dawn; rests up to 21 hours per day

**Breeding** One to 6 cubs (average 3–4) born after gestation period of 100–119 days. Weaned at 6–7 months; sexually mature at 3–4 years. May live up to 30 years in captivity, rarely more than 13 in the wild

**Voice** Variety of puffs, grunts, snarls, and roars

**Diet** Large mammal prey, including antelope, giraffe, zebra, hogs, and buffalo; also carrion

**Habitat** Savanna grasslands, open woodlands, desert margins, and scrub

**Distribution** Scattered populations in sub-Saharan Africa; population in Gir Forest, northwestern India

**Status** Population: several thousand; IUCN Vulnerable; CITES II. Asian lions fewer than 300; IUCN Endangered; CITES I. Declining outside protected areas

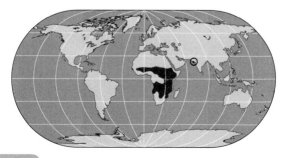

# Tiger

**Common name** Tiger

**Scientific name** *Panthera tigris*

**Family** Felidae

**Order** Carnivora

**Size** Length head/body: 4.6–9 ft (1.4–2.7 m); tail length: 23–43 in (60–110 cm); height at shoulder: 31–43 in (80–110 cm)

**Weight** Male 200–660 lb (90–300 kg); female 143–364 lb (65–165 kg)

**Key features** Huge, highly muscular cat with large head and long tail; unmistakable orange coat with dark stripes; underside white

**Habits** Solitary and highly territorial; active mostly at night; climbs and swims well

**Breeding** Litters of 1–6 (usually 2 or 3) cubs born at any time of year after gestation period of 95–110 days. Weaned at 3–6 months; females sexually mature at 3–4 years, males at 4–5 years. May live up to 26 years in captivity, rarely more than 10 in the wild

**Voice** Purrs, grunts, and blood-curdling roars

**Diet** Mainly large, hooved mammals, including deer, buffalo, antelope, and gaur

**Habitat** Tropical forests and swamps; grasslands with good vegetation cover and water nearby

**Distribution** India, Bhutan, Bangladesh, Nepal; China; southeastern Siberia; Myanmar (Burma), Vietnam, Laos, Thailand, and Sumatra

**Status** Population: 5,000–7,500; IUCN Endangered; CITES I. Previously hunted for fur and body parts, and to protect people and livestock

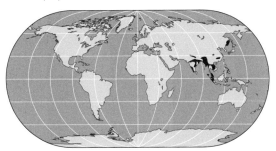

# Cheetah

**Common name** Cheetah

**Scientific name** *Acinonyx jubatus*

**Family** Felidae

**Order** Carnivora

**Size** Length head/body: 44–59 in (112–150 cm); tail length: 24–31 in (60–80 cm); height at shoulder: 26–37 in (67–94 cm)

**Weight** 46–159 lb (21–72 kg)

**Key features** Very slender, long-limbed cat with small head, rounded ears, and long tail held in low sweep; fur pale gold to tawny, paler on belly with black spots; end of tail has dark bands

**Habits** Diurnal; can be solitary and nomadic or live in small groups

**Breeding** Litters of 1–8 (usually 3–5) cubs born at any time of year after gestation period of 90–95 days. Weaned at 3–6 months; sexually mature at 18 months but rarely breeds before 2 years. May live up to 19 years in captivity, up to 14 in the wild, but usually many fewer

**Voice** Purrs, yelps, moans, and snarls; also a high-pitched churring; females use birdlike chirping to reassure young

**Diet** Mostly gazelles and impalas; other hoofed animals depending on opportunity

**Habitat** Savanna grassland, scrub, and semidesert

**Distribution** Widespread but scattered populations throughout sub-Saharan Africa, excluding the Congo Basin. Small population in Iran

**Status** Population: fewer than 15,000; IUCN Vulnerable; CITES I. Range and population greatly reduced, now protected in most of its range

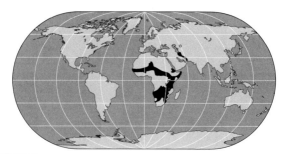

# Leopard

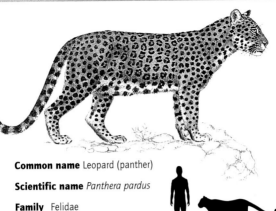

**Common name** Leopard (panther)

**Scientific name** *Panthera pardus*

**Family** Felidae

**Order** Carnivora

**Size** Length head/body: 35–75 in (90–190 cm); tail length: 23–43 in (58–110 cm); height at shoulder: 18–31 in (45–78 cm)

**Weight** Male 160–200 lb (73–90 kg); female 62–132 lb (28–60 kg)

**Key features** Large, lean cat with long tail; pale gold to tawny coat marked all over with black spots arranged into rosettes on back and flanks

**Habits** Solitary; mostly nocturnal; excellent climber

**Breeding** Litters of 1–6 (usually 2 or 3) young born after gestation period of 90–105 days during favorable season (varies throughout range). Weaned at 3 months; sexually mature at 3 years. May live over 20 years in captivity, probably well over 20 in the wild

**Voice** Rasping calls, grunts, and roars

**Diet** Mostly small- to medium-sized hoofed mammals; also monkeys, rabbits, rodents, and invertebrates, such as beetles

**Habitat** Varied; includes lowland forest, grassland, brush, and semidesert

**Distribution** Most of southern Asia and sub-Saharan Africa, excluding rain forests of Congo Basin. Small populations in North Africa, Middle East, Arabia, and China

**Status** Population: fewer than 700,000; IUCN Endangered and Critically Endangered (several subspecies); CITES I. Widespread but declining due to habitat loss and hunting

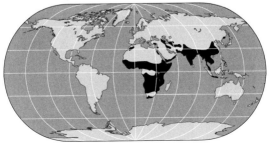

# Snow Leopard

**Common name** Snow leopard (ounce)

**Scientific name** *Panthera uncia*
*(Uncia uncia)*

**Family** Felidae

**Order** Carnivora

**Size** Length head/body: 39–51 in (100–130 cm); tail length: 31–39 in (80–100 cm); height at shoulder: 24 in (60 cm)

**Weight** Male 100–121 lb (45–55 kg); female 77–88 lb (35–40 kg)

**Key features** Long-bodied cat with relatively short legs, small head, and long tail; fur is thick and pale gray to creamy-white, with gray spots and rosettes all over body, except the underside

**Habits** Active dusk to dawn; solitary; very agile

**Breeding** Litters of 1–5 (usually 2 or 3) cubs born April–June after gestation period of 90–103 days. Weaned at 2–3 months; sexually mature at 2 years. May live up to 15 years in captivity, 21 in the wild

**Voice** Soft growls, grunts, and huffing sounds; moans loudly in courtship; does not roar

**Diet** Mountain animals, including goats, deer, pikas, and marmots; some domestic animals

**Habitat** Rocky mountainsides and grassy alpine plateaus at 9,000–20,000 ft (2,700–6,000 m)

**Distribution** Mountainous parts of China, Nepal, Bhutan, India, Pakistan, Afghanistan, Uzbekistan, Tajikistan, Kazakhstan, Russia, and Mongolia

**Status** Population: fewer than 7,000; IUCN Endangered; CITES I. In decline as a result of hunting; also persecuted by livestock farmers

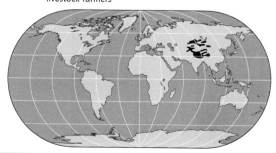

# Jaguar

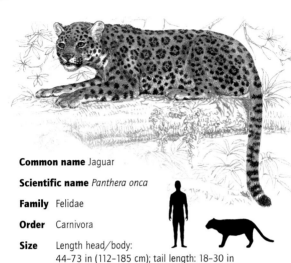

**Common name** Jaguar

**Scientific name** *Panthera onca*

**Family** Felidae

**Order** Carnivora

**Size** Length head/body: 44–73 in (112–185 cm); tail length: 18–30 in (45–75 cm); height at shoulder: 27–30 in (68–76 cm)

**Weight** Male 200–264 lb (90–120 kg); female 130–200 lb (60–90 kg)

**Key features** Large, robust-looking cat with short, thick tail and broad, heavy-looking head; fur pale gold to reddish-brown with spots arranged in rosettes and rings; black individuals known

**Habits** Solitary; territorial; active at any time of day but mostly around dawn and dusk; excellent swimmer and climber

**Breeding** Litters of 1–4 cubs born at any time of year in tropics after gestation period of 93–105 days (seasonal in north and south). Weaned at 5–6 months; sexually mature at 2–4 years. May live up to 22 years in captivity, 24 in the wild

**Voice** Grunts and mews

**Diet** Mostly peccaries and capybaras; also tapirs and other mammals; crocodiles and fish

**Habitat** Forests, scrub, grasslands, and semidesert; prefers habitats with water nearby

**Distribution** Central and South America south to northern Argentina and Paraguay

**Status** Population: unknown, probably several thousand; IUCN Lower Risk: near threatened; CITES I. Declining in range and population

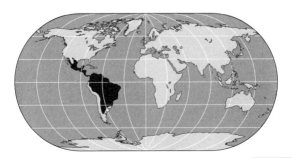

# Bobcat

**Common name** Bobcat

**Scientific name** *Felis rufus*

**Family** Felidae

**Order** Carnivora

**Size** Length head/body: 25.5–41 in (65–105 cm); tail length: 4–7.5 in (11–19 cm); height at shoulder: 17.5–23 in (45–58 cm)

**Weight** 9–33 lb (4–15 kg)

**Key features** Small, slender-limbed, short-tailed cat; fur thick, varies in color from buff to brown with darker spots and streaks; ears pointed, often with tufts; ruff of fur around jowls

**Habits** Solitary; territorial; active day or night

**Breeding** Litters of 1–6 kittens born after gestation period of 60–70 days, usually in spring. Weaned at 2 months; females sexually mature at 1 year, males at 2 years. May live up to 32 years in captivity, probably no more than 13 in the wild

**Voice** Usually silent, but hisses and shrieks in distress and during courtship

**Diet** Small mammals and birds; sometimes larger prey, such as small deer; domestic animals

**Habitat** Varied; includes forests, scrub, swamp, mountains, and the edges of deserts

**Distribution** North America

**Status** Population: 700,000–1 million; CITES II. Declined in the past due to persecution; still harvested for fur under license in some states

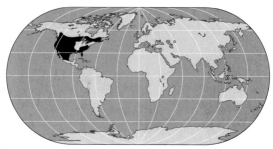

# Lynx

**Common name** Lynx (Eurasian lynx)

**Scientific name** *Felis lynx*

**Family** Felidae

**Order** Carnivora

**Size** Length head/body: 31–51 in (80–130 cm); tail length: 4–10 in (10–25 cm); height at shoulder: 23.5–29.5 in (60–75 cm)

**Weight** 18–84 lb (8–38 kg)

**Key features** Stocky cat with longish legs and large, furry feet; color varies from pale gray through yellow to reddish-brown; ears tufted

**Habits** Solitary; nocturnal; wanders widely

**Breeding** Litters of 1–4 kittens born April–June after gestation period of 67–74 days. Weaned at 3 months; females sexually mature at 9–21 months, males at 21–31 months. Lives up to 24 years in captivity, 17 in the wild

**Voice** Hisses and mews, but usually silent

**Diet** Mostly eats small- and medium-sized mammals, including hares and small deer

**Habitat** Mixed and taiga forest, scrub, steppe, and rocky alpine slopes

**Distribution** Eurasian lynx: northeastern Europe, Balkans, Turkey, and the Middle East excluding Arabia, much of former U.S.S.R., Mongolia, and northern China. Iberian lynx: Spain, Portugal. Canadian lynx: Canada, Alaska, northern U.S.

**Status** Population: unknown, but certainly many thousands; IUCN Endangered (Iberian), Vulnerable (Canadian); CITES I (Iberian), II (Canadian and Eurasian). All have declined, mainly as a result of hunting for fur

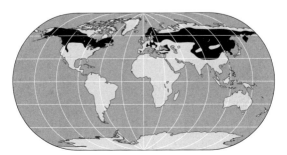

# Puma

**Common name** Puma (cougar, panther, mountain lion, catamount)

**Scientific name** *Felis concolor*

**Family** Felidae

**Order** Carnivora

**Size** Length head/body: 38–77 in (96–196 cm); tail length: 21–32 in (53–82 cm); height at shoulder: 24–27.5 in (60–70 cm)

**Weight** Male 148–264 lb (67–120 kg); female 80–132 lb (36–60 kg)

**Key features** Large, muscular cat with long legs and tail; small head with large, rounded ears; coat color varies from silvery gray through warm buffy tones to dark tawny

**Habits** Solitary; active at any time of day; climbs extremely well

**Breeding** Litters of 1–6 (usually 3 or 4) kittens born January–June after gestation period of 90–96 days. Weaned at 3 months; sexually mature at 2.5–3 years. May live up to 21 years in captivity, rarely more than 14 in the wild

**Voice** Hisses, growls, whistles, and screams

**Diet** Carnivorous; mostly deer; also other hoofed animals, rodents, and hares

**Habitat** Very varied; lowland and mountain forests, swamps, grassland, and scrub

**Distribution** Most of North and South America

**Status** Population: many thousands in total, but Florida panther (*F. c. coryi*) fewer than 50; IUCN Critically Endangered (2 subspecies); CITES II (at least 2 subspecies). Persecuted as a pest in the past; now protected in parts of its range although still hunted in other areas

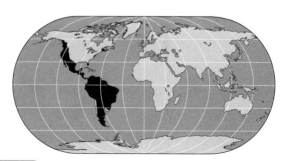

# Serval

**Common name** Serval

**Scientific name** *Felis serval*

**Family** Felidae

**Order** Carnivora

**Size** Length head/body: 26–39 in (67–100 cm); tail length: 9–18 in (24–45 cm); height at shoulder: 21–24.5 in (54–62 cm)

**Weight** 20–40 lb (9–18 kg)

**Key features** Slender, long-limbed cat with longish neck and very large, rounded ears; coat is light beige to dark gold, pale on underside, and marked with variable black spots and streaks; black rings on tail

**Habits** Active by day or night; solitary and territorial; performs leaps when hunting, displaying, and as a means of seeing over long grass

**Breeding** One or 2 litters of 1–4 kittens born each year after gestation period of 74 days. Weaned at 6 months; sexually mature at 2 years. May live up to 20 years in captivity, 13 in the wild

**Voice** Growls, purrs, and shrill, far-carrying calls

**Diet** Mostly mice; also small mammals and birds

**Habitat** Riverside grasslands and reed beds; savanna regions, mountain grasslands

**Distribution** Most of sub-Saharan Africa, excluding Congo Basin and large deserts such as the Namib, Karroo, and Kalahari. Small outlying population in Morocco

**Status** Population: abundant; IUCN Endangered (Morroccan subspecies); CITES II. Common, but declining due to hunting and habitat loss

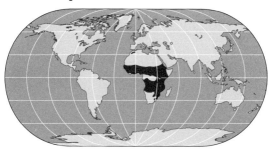

CARNIVORES
# Wildcat

**Common name**
  Wildcat

**Scientific name** *Felis silvestris*

**Family**  Felidae

**Order**  Carnivora

**Size**  Length head/body: 20–30 in
  (50–76 cm); tail length: 8–14 in
  (21–35 cm); height at shoulder: 15–22 in
  (38–56 cm)

**Weight**  6.6–17.6 lb (3–8 kg)

**Key features**  Smallish cat with thick fur, very similar to a
  domestic tabby; tail noticeably bushy with blunt end

**Habits**  Solitary; mainly active between dusk and dawn; excellent
  climber

**Breeding**  Litters of 1–8 kittens born after gestation period of
  61–68 days; births occur late spring in north, during
  rainy season in south, and year-round in tropics. Weaned
  at 30 days; sexually mature at 9–12 months. May live up
  to 15 years in captivity, fewer in the wild

**Voice**  Catlike mewing, hissing, and screeching

**Diet**  Mainly small mammals, especially rabbits and rodents;
  also birds, reptiles, and amphibians

**Habitat**  Forests, scrub, and open country with rocky crevices and
  patchy vegetation

**Distribution**  Scotland and southwestern Europe, including
  several Mediterranean islands; Africa (except for large
  deserts and tropical rain forests); Middle East and
  central and southern Asia, India, and north-central China

**Status**  Population: widespread and common; IUCN Vulnerable
  and CITES II (Scottish population). Globally abundant,
  but some local populations now very small

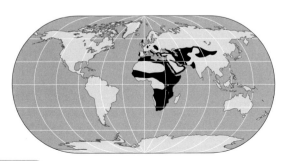

# Gray Wolf

**Common name** Gray wolf (timber wolf)

**Scientific name** *Canis lupus*

**Family** Canidae

**Order** Carnivora

**Size** Length head/body: 35-56 in (89-142 cm); tail length: 12-20 in (30-51 cm); height at shoulder: 23-28 in (58-77 cm)

**Weight** 22-175 lb (10-80 kg). Male larger than female

**Key features** Large, long-legged dog with thick fur and bushy tail; fur usually gray, although color varies with distribution

**Habits** Social, although sometimes solitary; more or less nocturnal; hunts communally to bring down prey up to 10 times its own weight

**Breeding** One to 11 (average 6) pups born in a den after gestation period of 63 days. Weaned at 5 weeks; sexually mature at 2 years. May live up to 16 years in captivity, rarely more than 13 in the wild

**Voice** Growls, barks, whines, and howls

**Diet** Mainly large mammal prey, including deer, moose, muskox, mountain sheep, bison, beavers, and hares

**Habitat** Almost anywhere from tundra to scrub, grassland, mountains, and forest

**Distribution** Northern Hemisphere

**Status** Population: many thousands; IUCN Vulnerable; CITES I (India, Pakistan, Nepal, Bhutan); elsewhere CITES II. Now more stable following centuries of persecution

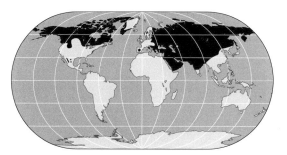

# Coyote

**Common name** Coyote

**Scientific name** *Canis latrans*

**Family** Canidae

**Order** Carnivora

**Size** Length head/body: 30–39 in (76–100 cm); tail length: 12–19 in (30–48 cm); height at shoulder: about 24 in (60 cm)

**Weight** 15.5–44 lb (7–20 kg). Male slightly larger than female

**Key features** Typical wolf but smaller and slighter in build than gray wolf; ears large and pointed; muzzle narrow; fur shaggy and usually a shade of beige or gray; paler on belly, but darkening to black on tip of tail

**Habits** Mostly nocturnal, but can be active at any time of day; some migrate into mountains in summer; less social than gray wolf

**Breeding** Litters of 2–12 (average 6) born in spring after gestation period of 63 days. Weaned at 5–6 weeks; sexually mature at 1 or 2 years. May live up to 21 years in captivity, usually fewer than 15 in the wild

**Voice** Wide repertoire of barks, whines, and howls

**Diet** Carnivorous; mostly mammals, including rabbits, woodchucks, rodents, and deer; also carrion

**Habitat** Grasslands and prairie, scrub, and forest

**Distribution** North America

**Status** Population: abundant. Common and widespread; hunted for fur and as a pest

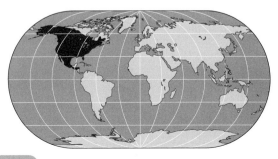

# Black-Backed Jackal

**Common name** Black-backed jackal

**Scientific name** *Canis mesomelas*

**Family** Canidae

**Order** Carnivora

**Size** Length head/body: 18–35.5 in (45–90 cm); tail length: 12–19 in (30–48 cm); height at shoulder: 10–16 in (26–40 cm)

**Weight** 13–29 lb (6–13.5 kg)

**Key features** Small and foxlike with slender legs, pointed face, and large triangular ears; coat rough and reddish-gray, except for dark patch on back extending to tip of tail

**Habits** Active at any time of day; lives alone or in small family groups; territorial

**Breeding** One to 8 (usually 4) young born at the start of the rainy season after gestation period of 60 days. Weaned at 8–9 weeks; sexually mature at 11 months. May live up to 14 years in captivity, usually fewer than 8 in the wild

**Voice** Eerie-sounding barks and howls

**Diet** Varied: mammalian prey (from mice to small antelope); also dead meat; invertebrates such as beetles, grubs, and worms; plant material

**Habitat** Tropical grassland and open woodland

**Distribution** Two distinct ranges; the first includes parts of Kenya, Tanzania, Somalia, and Ethiopia; the other falls in parts of South Africa, Namibia, Botswana, Angola, and Zimbabwe

**Status** Population: abundant and common; persecuted as vermin, especially by sheep farmers

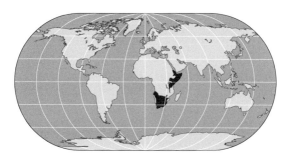

# Red Fox

**Common name**
Red fox

**Scientific name** *Vulpes vulpes*

**Family** Canidae

**Order** Carnivora

**Size** Length head/body: 18-35.5 in
(45-90 cm); tail length:
12-21.5 in (30-55 cm); height at shoulder:
up to 14 in (36 cm)

**Weight** 7-31 lb (3-14 kg)

**Key features** Typical fox with long, narrow body ending in thick, brushy tail; pointed muzzle and ears; neat legs and feet; fur typically red, but varies from deep gold to dark brown, fading to white on muzzle, chest, and belly; often darker on legs; black and pale variants known

**Habits** Mostly nocturnal; sometimes lives in family groups; but usually hunts alone; nonbreeding males are solitary

**Breeding** Litters of 1-12 (usually 3-7) cubs born in spring after gestation period of 51-53 days. Weaned at 8-10 weeks; sexually mature at 10 months. May live up to 12 years in captivity, rarely more than 5 in the wild

**Voice** Barks, whines, yelps, screams, excited "gekkering" when playing

**Diet** Omnivorous; rodents and other small mammals; also insects, worms, and fruit

**Habitat** Diverse; includes farmland, forest, grassland, moorland, tundra, and urban areas

**Distribution** Europe and North America; also parts of Africa and Asia; introduced to Australia

**Status** Population: abundant. Persecuted as vermin; also hunted for sport

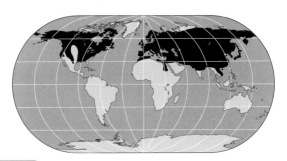

# Swift Fox

**Common name** Swift fox (kit fox)

**Scientific name** *Vulpes velox*

**Family** Canidae

**Order** Carnivora

**Size** Length head/body: 15–21 in (38–52 cm); tail length: 9–14 in (22–35 cm); height at shoulder: 12 in (30 cm)

**Weight** 4–7 lb (2–3 kg)

**Key features** Similar to red fox; winter coat grayish-beige with pale undersides and rich orange-brown on legs, tail, and flanks; summer coat shorter and darker; bushy tail tipped with black and slightly shorter than in other foxes

**Habits** Active at night; social, bold, and tame

**Breeding** Three to 6 young born in spring after gestation period of 50–60 days. Weaned at 6–7 weeks; sexually mature at 10 months. May live up to 14 years in captivity, usually fewer than 6 in the wild

**Voice** Quiet yelps and barks

**Diet** Small mammals, especially rabbits, pikas, and rodents; also birds, lizards, amphibians, insects, and occasionally plant material

**Habitat** Prairie and grassland

**Distribution** Scattered populations across central plains of the U.S. and Canada

**Status** Population: low thousands; IUCN Endangered (northern subspecies), elsewhere Lower Risk: conservation dependent; CITES I (northern subspecies)

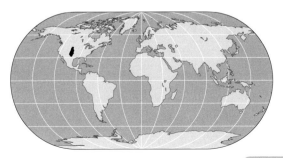

# Arctic Fox

**Common name** Arctic fox

**Scientific name** *Vulpes (Alopex) lagopus*

**Family** Canidae

**Order** Carnivora

**Size** Length head/body: 18–27 in (46–68 cm); tail length: 12 in (30 cm); height at shoulder: 11 in (28 cm)

**Weight** 3–20 lb (1.4–9 kg)

**Key features** Stout-looking fox with short legs, long, bushy tail, small, rounded ears, and a thick, woolly coat; fur pure white in winter in high Arctic animals; fur extends to soles of feet

**Habits** Social; sometimes migratory; active at any time of day; does not hibernate

**Breeding** Litters of 6–12 (occasionally as many as 25) pups born in early summer after gestation period of 49–57 days. Weaned at 2–4 weeks; sexually mature at 10 months. May live up to 16 years in captivity, fewer in the wild

**Voice** Barks, whines, screams, and hisses

**Diet** Mainly carnivorous; prey includes seals, rodents (especially lemmings), seabirds, fish, invertebrates such as crabs, mollusks, and insects, and carrion; scavenges from kills made by other Arctic predators; occasionally plant material

**Habitat** Arctic and northern alpine tundra, boreal forest, ice cap, and even sea ice

**Distribution** Arctic regions of Canada, Alaska, Greenland, Iceland, Finland, Sweden, Norway, and Russia

**Status** Population: abundant. Generally common, although range and population size have declined recently. Protected in Norway, Sweden, and Finland; hunted for fur and as vermin elsewhere

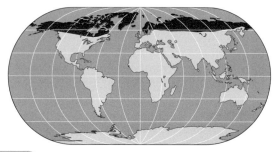

# Fennec Fox

**Common name** Fennec fox

**Scientific name** *Vulpes (Fennecus) zerda*

**Family** Canidae

**Order** Carnivora

**Size** Length head/body: 14–16 in (35–41 cm); tail length: 7–12 in (18–30.5 cm); height at shoulder: 10 in (25 cm)

**Weight** 2.2–3.3 lb (1–1.5 kg)

**Key features** Small, dainty fox with huge, triangular ears and a long, bushy tail tipped with black; thick, pale, reddish-beige to white fur; soles of feet are also fur covered

**Habits** Social and territorial; nocturnal; lives in burrows

**Breeding** Two to 5 pups born in spring after gestation period of 50–52 days. Weaned at 9–10 weeks; sexually mature at 11 months. May live up to 14 years in captivity, probably about 8–10 in the wild

**Voice** Barks and whines; screams when fighting

**Diet** Small mammals, birds, reptiles, eggs, insects, and plant material

**Habitat** Desert and semidesert

**Distribution** Sahara Desert and North Africa, including parts of Morocco, Algeria, Tunisia, Mali, Niger, Libya, Chad, Egypt, and the Sudan

**Status** Population: widespread but uncommon; CITES II. A species in decline

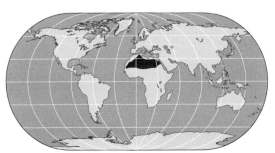

# Bat-Eared Fox

**Common name** Bat-eared fox

**Scientific name** *Otocyon megalotis*

**Family** Canidae

**Order** Carnivora

**Size** Length head/body: 18–26 in (46–66 cm); tail length: 9–13.5 in (23–34 cm); height at shoulder: 12–16 in (30–40 cm)

**Weight** 6.6–11.6 lb (3–5.3 kg)

**Key features** Small, short-legged dog with thick, fuzzy-looking coat; fur is yellowish-brown but black on legs, feet, tail tip, and ears; small face with short muzzle; huge ears

**Habits** Social; generally active at night, but southern population is active during the day in winter

**Breeding** Litters of 2–6 pups born after gestation period of 60–70 days; births in September to November in southern Africa, all year round in the east. Weaned at 10 weeks; sexually mature at 9 months. May live up to 14 years in captivity, many fewer in the wild

**Voice** Soft whistling calls

**Diet** Mostly termites; also other invertebrates (such as dung beetles); some small mammals, birds, eggs, and plant material

**Habitat** Dry tropical grassland and scrub

**Distribution** East Africa: southern parts of Ethiopia and the Sudan; Somalia and Tanzania. Southern Africa: southern Angola, Zimbabwe, Botswana, Namibia, South Africa, and western Mozambique

**Status** Population: abundant. Secure, even expanding its range in places

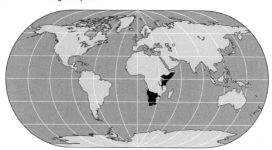

# African Wild Dog

**Common name** African wild dog (African hunting dog, painted hunting dog)

**Scientific name** *Lycaon pictus*

**Family** Canidae

**Order** Carnivora

**Size** Length head/body: 30–44 in (76–112 cm); tail length: 12–16 in (30–41 cm); height at shoulder: 24–31 in (61–78 cm)

**Weight** 37.5–80 lb (17–36 kg)

**Key features** Lean, long-legged dog with large ears and 4 toes on each foot (other dogs have 5 digits on front feet); fur is short, thin, and patterned with variable blotches and speckles of black, brown, yellow, and white; dark skin often shows through coat

**Habits** Highly social; active by day; packs wander widely except when breeding

**Breeding** Litters of up to 20 pups (usually 4–8) born at any time of year after gestation period of 79–80 days. Weaned at 11 weeks; sexually mature at 2 years. May live up to 17 years in captivity, 11 in the wild

**Voice** Excited squeaks and twitters; also hoots and wails that carry long distances

**Diet** Carnivorous, mostly taking hoofed mammals such as antelope

**Habitat** Savanna grassland and open woodland

**Distribution** Africa south of the Sahara

**Status** Population: probably fewer than 5,000 and declining; IUCN Endangered. Protected by law in most of its range

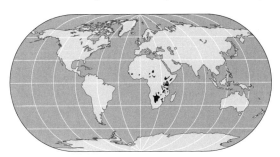

# Dingo

**Common name** Dingo

**Scientific name** *Canis dingo (C. lupus dingo)*

**Family** Canidae

**Order** Carnivora

**Size** Length head/body: 34–48 in (86–122 cm); tail length: 10–15 in (26–38 cm); height at shoulder: 17–25 in (44–63 cm)

**Weight** 22–53 lb (10–24 kg)

**Key features** Large robust-looking dog; sandy fur with pale markings on feet, chest, muzzle, and tail tip; long muzzle and pricked ears; bushy tail

**Habits** Lives in packs of up to 12, defending common territory; hunts alone or in packs

**Breeding** One to 10 (average 5) pups born in underground den during winter after gestation period of 63 days. Weaned at 3 months; sexually mature at 2 years. May live a little over 14 years in captivity, up to 14 in the wild

**Voice** Typical doglike bark, whines, yelps, and howls

**Diet** Varies according to prey available; anything from kangaroos and rabbits to insects and carrion

**Habitat** Diverse; hot deserts, tropical and temperate forests, mountains, scrub, and ranch land

**Distribution** Australia, New Guinea, Indochina, Indonesia, Borneo, and Philippines

**Status** Population: abundant. Declining in numbers, but not included in any conservation programs because most countries do not protect introduced or alien species

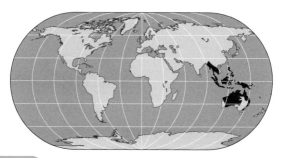

# Polar Bear

**Common name** Polar bear

**Scientific name** *Ursus maritimus*

**Family** Ursidae

**Order** Carnivora

**Size** Length head/body: 6.6–8.2 ft (2–2.5 m); tail length: 3–5 in (7–13 cm); height at shoulder: up to 5.2 ft (1.6 m)

**Weight** Male 660–1,760 lb (300–800 kg); female 330–660 lb (50–300 kg)

**Key features** Huge bear with thick, off-white coat; head relatively small; feet large and furry

**Habits** Solitary; migratory and partially nomadic; pregnant females hibernate in winter; excellent swimmer

**Breeding** Litters of 1–4 tiny cubs born in midwinter after gestation period of 195–265 days (includes variable period of delayed implantation). Weaned from 6 months; sexually mature at 5–6 years. May live up to 45 years in captivity, 30 in the wild

**Voice** Grunts and growls

**Diet** Carnivorous: mainly seals but occasionally other animals such as reindeer; also fish, seabirds, carrion, and plant material in summer

**Habitat** Sea ice, ice cap, and tundra; equally at home in water and on land

**Distribution** Arctic Circle; parts of Canada, Alaska, Russia, Scandinavia, and Greenland

**Status** Population: 20,000–30,000; IUCN Lower Risk: conservation dependent; CITES II. Main threat is from human exploitation of Arctic habitats

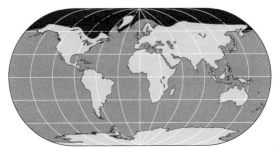

# American Black Bear

**Common name** American black bear

**Scientific name** *Ursus americanus*

**Family** Ursidae

**Order** Carnivora

**Size** Length head/body: 4.9–5.9 ft (1.5–1.8 m); tail length: 4.5 in (12 cm); height at shoulder: up to 36 in (91 cm)

**Weight** Male 250–600 lb (113–272 kg); female 200–310 lb (91–141 kg)

**Key features** Large bear with thick, but not shaggy coat; fur can be variety of colors, but usually brown or black; muzzle less furry than rest of face

**Habits** Solitary; most active at night; swims and climbs well; hibernates over winter

**Breeding** Litters of 1–5 (usually 2 or 3) cubs born after gestation period of 220 days (including about 150 days delayed implantation). Weaned at 6–8 months; females sexually mature at 4–5 years, males at 5–6 years. May live up to 31 years in captivity, 26 in the wild

**Voice** Various grunts, rumbling growls, and woofing sounds; cubs give high-pitched howls

**Diet** Mostly plant material, including fruit, nuts, grass, bark, and roots; fish; invertebrates such as insects and their larvae and worms; also honey, other mammals, and carrion

**Habitat** Forest and scrub; occasionally open spaces

**Distribution** Canada, Alaska, and U.S. south to Mexico

**Status** Population: 400,000–500,000; CITES II. Still common, but population now reduced due to hunting, persecution, and habitat loss

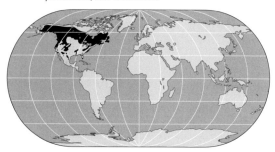

# Brown Bear

**Common name** Brown bear (grizzly bear, big brown bear)

**Scientific name** *Ursus arctos*

**Family** Ursidae

**Order** Carnivora

**Size** Length head/body:
5.5–9.3 ft (1.7–2.8 m); tail length: 2.5–8 in (6–20 cm);
height at shoulder: 35–60 in (90–150 cm). Male bigger
than female

**Weight** 132–1,750 lb (60–800 kg)

**Key features** Medium to large bear with shaggy, light-brown to
black fur, often grizzled (grayish) on back and shoulders;
narrow snout; broad face

**Habits** Solitary; nonterritorial; hibernates over winter

**Breeding** Litters of 1–4 (usually 2) cubs born January–March
after gestation period of 180–266 days. Weaned at 5
months; sexually mature at 4–6 years. May live up to 40
years in captivity, 25 in the wild

**Voice** Various grunts and growls

**Diet** Mostly plant material, including grass, roots, and fungi;
also small invertebrates, fish, and carrion

**Habitat** Varied; tundra, open plains, alpine grassland, forests,
and wooded areas

**Distribution** Western Canada, Alaska, and northwestern U.S.;
northern Asia south of Arctic Circle; Scandinavia, eastern
Europe, and Middle East; Pyrenees, Alps, and Abruzzi
Mountains

**Status** Population: 220,000; CITES I (several Eurasian
subspecies); CITES II (North American subspecies).
Declining, but now more stable

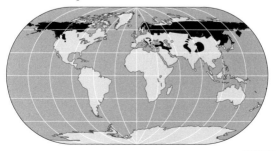

# Giant Panda

**Common name**
Giant panda
(panda, panda bear)

**Scientific name**
*Ailuropoda melanoleuca*

**Family** Ursidae

**Order** Carnivora

**Size** Length head/body: 47–59 in
(120–150 cm); tail length: 5 in
(13 cm); height at shoulder: up to 27.5–31 in
(70–80 cm)

**Weight** 165–350 lb (75–160 kg)

**Key features** Unmistakable large, furry bear with black legs, shoulder band, eye patches, and ears; body is off-white

**Habits** Solitary; nonterritorial; active between dusk and dawn; climbs well

**Breeding** One or 2 cubs born August–September after gestation period of 97–163 days (includes variable period of delayed implantation). Weaned at 8–9 months; sexually mature at 6–7 years. May live up to 34 years in captivity, fewer in the wild

**Voice** Varied sounds, including growls, moans, barks, squeaks, and bleats

**Diet** Omnivorous, but mostly bamboo and some other plant material; occasionally small animals

**Habitat** Mountainside forests with bamboo thickets at altitudes of 3,300–13,000 ft (1,000–3,900 m)

**Distribution** Small remaining range in central China

**Status** Population: about 1,000; IUCN Endangered; CITES I. Has declined greatly in range and population due to hunting, habitat loss, and specialized lifestyle

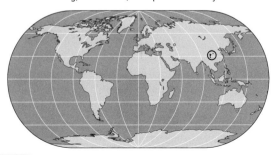

# Striped Hyena

**Common name** Striped hyena

**Scientific name** *Hyaena hyaena*

**Family** Hyaenidae

**Order** Carnivora

**Size** Length head/body: 39-47 in (100-120 cm); tail length: 10-14 in (25-35 cm); height at shoulder: 26-30 in (66-75 cm)

**Weight** 55-119 lb (25-54 kg)

**Key features** A tall, slender hyena with thick neck, large eyes, and bold stripes; fur is long and shaggy with a high hairy crest extending down the middle of the neck and back; face and throat often black; tail white

**Habits** Solitary or lives in small clans of closely related individuals

**Breeding** One to 5 (usually 3) cubs born at any time of year after gestation period of 90 days. Weaned at 10 to 12 months; sexually mature at 2-3 years. May live up to 24 years in captivity, probably up to about 15 in the wild

**Voice** Generally quiet; occasionally growls or whines

**Diet** An omnivorous scavenger; takes small prey, but may kill larger animals; fruit and bones

**Habitat** Dry grassland and semidesert; also rocky hills

**Distribution** North and northeastern Africa; Middle East and Turkey east to India; up to 10,000 ft (3,000 m) in some mountainous areas

**Status** Population: relatively abundant. Has declined in numbers and distribution, but is still widespread and fairly numerous

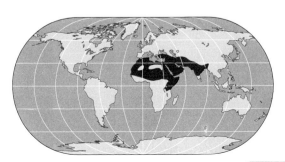

# Spotted Hyena

**Common name** Spotted hyena

**Scientific name** *Crocuta crocuta*

**Family** Hyaenidae

**Order** Carnivora

**Size** Length head/body: 39–71 in (100–180 cm); tail length: 10–14 in (25–36 cm); height at shoulder: 28–35 in (70–90 cm)

**Weight** 88–200 lb (40–91 kg); female generally about 12% heavier than male

**Key features** Doglike, powerfully built animal with short tail and sloping back; pale sandy gray coat with dark, irregular blotches

**Habits** Usually nocturnal, but will venture out during the daytime; lives in clans

**Breeding** Usually 2, but up to 4 cubs born after gestation period of 4 months. Weaned at 8–18 months; sexually mature at 2 years. May live to over 40 years in captivity, probably fewer in the wild

**Voice** Loud whooping noises; crazy-sounding giggle

**Diet** Meat from carcasses killed by other predators; slow animals like waterbuck; also tortoises, fish, insects, and garbage

**Habitat** Acacia savannas; urban fringes

**Distribution** Africa south of Sahara, except for areas of thick forest; absent from most of South Africa

**Status** Population: several thousand; IUCN Lower Risk: conservation dependent. Widespread and fairly common, but disappearing from many places being unpopular with farmers

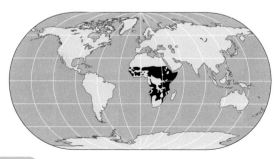

# Aardwolf

**Common name** Aardwolf

**Scientific name** *Proteles cristata*

**Family** Hyaenidae

**Order** Carnivora

**Size** Length head/body: 22–31 in (55–80 cm); tail length: 8–12 in (20–30 cm); height at shoulder: 16–20 in (40–50 cm)

**Weight** 18–26 lb (8–12 kg)

**Key features** Slender, creamy-brown animal with a few widely spaced black stripes; black feet, muzzle, and tail tip; coat often discolored by soil from den; molar teeth small and peglike

**Habits** Nocturnal; territorial; normally forages alone

**Breeding** Two to 5 young born after gestation period of about 2–3 months. Weaned at 2–3 months; sexually mature at 1 year. May live up to 20 years in captivity, fewer in the wild

**Voice** Generally silent, but growls and barks when angry

**Diet** Mainly termites; some other insects, including beetles and grasshoppers; occasionally mice

**Habitat** Areas of dry, grazed grassland where termites are abundant

**Distribution** Southern Africa; separate subspecies in East Africa north to Eritrea

**Status** Population: widespread, but generally scarce, although not seriously threatened

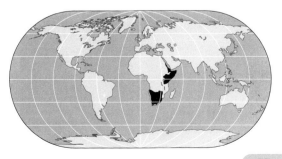

# Common Raccoon

**Common name** Common raccoon

**Scientific name** *Procyon lotor*

**Family** Procyonidae

**Order** Carnivora

**Size** Length head/body:
18–27 in (45–68 cm);
tail length: 8–12 in (20–30 cm); height at shoulder:
about 10–12 in (25–30 cm). Male about 25% larger
than female

**Weight** 11–18 lb (5–8 kg), but sometimes up to 33 lb (15 kg)

**Key features** Black "bandit" face mask, accentuated by gray
bars above and below; black eyes; short, rounded ears;
bushy tail with alternate brown and black rings (usually
5); body hairs long and gray

**Habits** Nocturnal; mainly solitary, although related females may
live close to one another

**Breeding** Four to 6 young born around February to April after
gestation period of 63 days. Weaned at 7 weeks;
females usually sexually mature by their first spring,
males by 2 years. May live over 17 years in captivity, up
to 16 in the wild

**Voice** Chitters, purrs, hisses, barks, growls, snarls, and squeaks

**Diet** Fruit, berries, nuts, and seeds; fish, crayfish, clams, snails,
and earthworms; crops such as corn and stored grain

**Habitat** Almost anywhere in North America, including
urban areas

**Distribution** Southern Canada, U.S., and Central America

**Status** Population: abundant. Most common member of
raccoon family; continues to expand its range and
increase in numbers

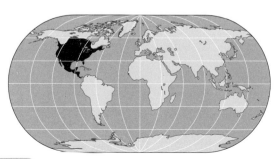

# Ringtailed Coati

**Common name** Ringtailed coati (coatimundi)

**Scientific name** *Nasua nasua*

**Family** Procyonidae

**Order** Carnivora

**Size** Length head/body:
16–26 in (41–67 cm);
tail length: 12.5–27 in (32–69 cm); height at shoulder:
up to 12 in (30 cm). Male generally larger than female

**Weight** 7–13 lb (3–6 kg)

**Key features** Long, flexible snout; long, banded tail; stocky,
reddish-brown to black upper body, yellowing
underneath; coat has coarse, long hairs; distinctive
white muzzle, chin, and throat

**Habits** Active throughout the day; females form gangs with
juveniles; males are often solitary

**Breeding** Births occur mainly April to June, perhaps earlier
farther south; 2–7 young born after gestation period
of about 74 days. Weaned at 4 months; sexually mature
at 2 years. May live over 17 years in captivity, 9–15 in
the wild

**Voice** Grunts and chittering used to maintain contact with
group, also snarls and squeaks; if threatened, will
indicate alarm by barking

**Diet** Woodland invertebrates (e.g., earthworms, millipedes,
snails); frogs and lizards caught with forepaws; adult
males tend to prey on large rodents; very fond of fruit

**Habitat** Woodlands

**Distribution** Colombia south to Argentina and Uruguay

**Status** Population: abundant. Generally common and
quite widespread

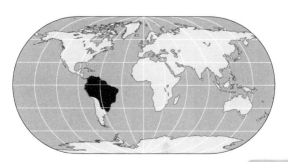

# Red Panda

**Common name** Red panda (lesser panda)

**Scientific name** *Ailurus fulgens*

**Family** Procyonidae (sometimes considered a member of the bear family, Ursidae)

**Order** Carnivora

**Size** Length head/body: 20–24 in (50–60 cm); tail length: 12–20 in (30–51 cm); height at shoulder: about 10–12 in (25–30 cm)

**Weight** 6–13 lb (3–6 kg)

**Key features** Vaguely raccoonlike animal the size of a large domestic cat; bright chestnut-colored fur, darker on belly; tail banded chestnut and cream; face has cream and white "mask"

**Habits** Arboreal and nocturnal; spends most of day sleeping in trees and feeds there at night

**Breeding** One to 4 young born in spring and summer (peaks in June) after gestation period of 114–145 days. Weaned at 4 months; sexually mature at 18 months. May live for 17 years in captivity, 8–14 in the wild

**Voice** Normally silent

**Diet** Bamboo shoots and leaves; fruit, berries, and flowers; birds, eggs, and small mammals

**Habitat** Temperate forests, both deciduous and conifer, often on steep slopes

**Distribution** Himalayan regions of Nepal, Bhutan, India, Laos, Myanmar (Burma), and China (Sichuan and Yunnan Provinces)

**Status** Population: unknown, but unlikely to exceed a few thousand; IUCN Endangered; CITES I

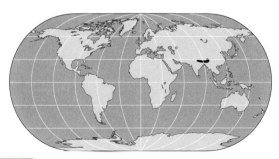

# Least Weasel

**Common name** Least weasel (European common weasel)

**Scientific name** *Mustela nivalis*

**Family** Mustelidae

**Order** Carnivora

**Size** Length head/ body: 7–10 in (17–25 cm); tail length: 1–5 in (3–12 cm)

**Weight** 1.7–3 oz (48–85 g)

**Key features** Long, sleek body with short legs and short tail; flat, narrow head; fur reddish-brown in summer, with creamy-white neck and belly; turns white in winter in northern populations

**Habits** Solitary, territorial animals; fierce predators; very active both day and night all year round

**Breeding** Up to 2 litters of 1–9 young born each year after gestation period of 34–37 days. Weaned at 3–4 weeks; females sexually mature at 4 months, males at 8 months. May live up to 10 years in captivity, usually under a year in the wild

**Voice** Low trill to signal a friendly meeting between a male and a female; loud, harsh chirp or screech when disturbed or ready to attack

**Diet** Mainly small rodents, especially mice; also rabbits, lemmings, moles, pikas, birds, fish, lizards, and insects

**Habitat** Almost anywhere providing suitable cover and access to rodents, including meadows, farmlands, prairies, marshes, and woodlands

**Distribution** Northern Hemisphere: Canada, Alaska, Siberia, Japan, northern U.S., northern Europe, and Russia

**Status** Population: abundant. One of the more numerous small carnivores

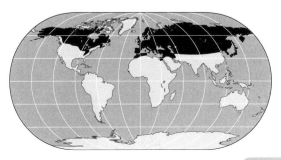

# Stoat

**Common name** Stoat (ermine, short-tailed weasel)

**Scientific name** *Mustela erminea*

**Family** Mustelidae

**Order** Carnivora

**Size** Length head/body: 7–12.5 in (17–32 cm); tail length: 1.5–5 in (4–12 cm)

**Weight** 1.5–12 oz (42–340 g)

**Key features** Lithe, long-bodied animal with short legs and longish, black-tipped tail; body fur rich brown with cream on belly; may turn brilliant white in winter; small head with round ears, large eyes, and long whiskers

**Habits** Mainly nocturnal; terrestrial, but can swim and climb well; active and agile; a territorial, fierce, and solitary predator

**Breeding** Single litter of 3–18 (usually 4–9) young born in spring after gestation period of 10 months (including delayed implantation). Weaned at 6–8 weeks; females sexually mature at 2–3 months, males at 12 months. May live up to 10 years in captivity, many fewer in the wild

**Voice** Shrill squeaks when excited

**Diet** Carnivorous; includes small mammals, especially rodents and rabbits; also birds and eggs, reptiles and amphibians

**Habitat** Varied; from Arctic tundra and moorland to forests and meadows

**Distribution** Northern Hemisphere (Eurasia and North America) from within Arctic Circle to latitude 30°N

**Status** Population: abundant. Common and widespread, but trapped for fur in some areas

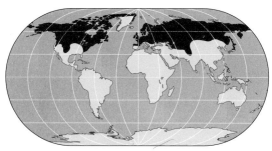

# Polecat

**Common name** Polecat

**Scientific name** *Mustela putorius*

**Family** Mustelidae

**Order** Carnivora

**Size** Length head/body: 12–18 in (30–46 cm); tail length: 5–6 in (12–14 cm). Male generally larger than female

**Weight** 1–3 lb (0.5–1.4 kg)

**Key features** Resembles short-legged cat, with a long, sinuous body; almost black in summer, but pale cream in winter; bold, dark mask pattern on face throughout the year

**Habits** Mainly nocturnal; solitary; forages along the ground; occasionally climbs

**Breeding** One litter per year of 3–7 (can be up to 12) young born about June after gestation period of 42 days. Weaned at 1 month; sexually mature at 1 year. May live up to 14 years in captivity, 5 in the wild

**Voice** May squeak and hiss occasionally, but sound is not used for social communication

**Diet** Mainly rabbits and voles; also birds, frogs, occasionally eels caught in wet grass; whatever is most abundant and easiest to catch

**Habitat** Young forestry plantations and woodland, but mainly on farmland where there is plenty of cover in hedges, walls, and old buildings

**Distribution** Western Europe from Britain and Spain east to the Black Sea and Baltic countries

**Status** Population: abundant. Previously eradicated from Scotland and most of England, but now recolonizing, thanks to reduced persecution

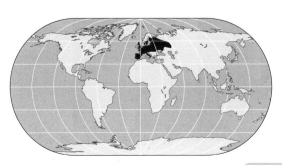

# American Marten

**Common name**
American marten (American pine marten, American sable)

**Scientific name** *Martes americana*

**Family** Mustelidae

**Order** Carnivora

**Size** Length head/body: 20–27 in (50–68 cm); tail length: 7–9 in (18–23 cm)

**Weight** 10–44 oz (280–1,250 g). Male generally at least a third bigger than female

**Key features** Slender cat-sized animal with short legs and bushy tail; fur ranges from pale brown to almost black with an orange or yellowish throat patch

**Habits** Active throughout the year and also at any time of day or night; climbs well

**Breeding** Up to 5 (usually 3) young born once a year in the spring after gestation period of 1 month. Weaned at 6 weeks; sexually mature at 15–24 months. May live 17 years in captivity, at least 15 in the wild

**Voice** Normally silent; sometimes makes chuckling noises or gives the occasional scream

**Diet** Wide variety of small animals; also insects, fruit, and seeds

**Habitat** Deciduous and coniferous forests

**Distribution** From Alaska eastward to eastern Canada; also Rocky Mountains and Sierra Nevada

**Status** Population: abundant. Widespread but elusive; rare and declining in some places

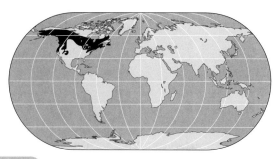

# Fisher

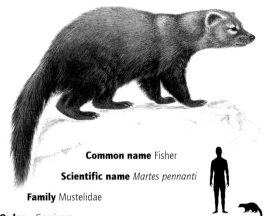

**Common name** Fisher

**Scientific name** *Martes pennanti*

**Family** Mustelidae

**Order** Carnivora

**Size** Length head/body: 18.5–29.5 in (47–75 cm); tail length: 12–16.5 in (30–42 cm)

**Weight** Male 7.7–12 lb (3.5–5.5 kg), occasionally up to 19.8 lb (9 kg); female 4.4–5.5 lb (2–2.5 kg)

**Key features** Cat-sized weasel with short legs, long body, and long, bushy tail; head is wedge shaped, relatively large, rounded ears; coat is dark and varies between sexes, seasons, and individuals

**Habits** Active any time of day in short bouts of 2–5 hours; territorial and mainly solitary, only meeting during the mating season; mainly ground dwelling, but climbs trees with ease

**Breeding** One litter per year of 1–5 pups born in spring after gestation period of 352 days (including an uncertain period of delayed implantation). Weaned at 2–4 months; females sexually mature at 1 year, males at 2 years. May live for 10 years in captivity, similar in the wild

**Voice** Growls, hissing coughs, or clicks, but normally silent

**Diet** Porcupines, snowshoe hares, and small rodents; also carrion, birds, eggs, insects, reptiles, and amphibians; some fruit and nuts

**Habitat** Mature forest and swampy woodlands

**Distribution** Northern U.S. and Canada; distribution extends south in mountainous regions

**Status** Population: unknown, perhaps tens of thousands. Protected in some U.S. states

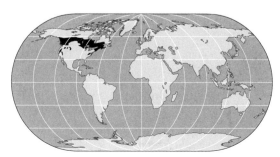

# American Mink

**Common name** American mink

**Scientific name** *Mustela vison*

**Family** Mustelidae

**Order** Carnivora

**Size** Length head/body: 12–18.5 in (30–47 cm); tail length: 5–9 in (13–23 cm)

**Weight** 1.9–4 lb (0.9–1.8 kg); female 1–1.8 lb (0.5–0.8 kg)

**Key features** Resembles short-legged, glossy black or dark-brown cat; pointed muzzle

**Habits** Mainly nocturnal; swims and dives; uses burrows and lairs among tree roots at water's edge, also rabbit burrows, but does not dig for itself

**Breeding** One litter of 4–6 young born April–May after gestation period of 39–78 days, including a variable period of delayed implantation. Weaned at 5–6 weeks; sexually mature at 2 years. May live for 10 years in captivity, 2–3 in the wild

**Voice** Hisses when threatened; may scream defiantly in self-defense, but usually silent

**Diet** Fish, frogs, small mammals, waterside birds and their eggs; also some invertebrates such as beetles and worms, especially along coasts

**Habitat** Mostly lowland areas beside rivers, lakes, and ponds; also marshland and along seashores

**Distribution** Canada; eastern and most of central U.S.; introduced to Europe: in Britain, France, Italy, Spain, Ireland, Scandinavia, and Iceland

**Status** Population: abundant. Increasing in Europe

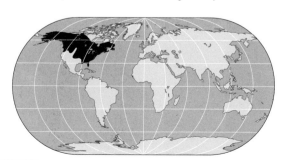

# Wolverine

**Common name** Wolverine (glutton, skunk bear)

**Scientific name** *Gulo gulo*

**Family** Mustelidae

**Order** Carnivora

**Size** Length head/body: 24–26 in
(62–67 cm); tail length: 5–10 in
(13–25 cm); height at shoulder: 14–17 in (35–43 cm)

**Weight** 20–65 lb (9–29 kg). Male at least 10% bigger
than female

**Key features** Low, thickset animal with short legs and large,
powerful paws; coat dark brown but paler on face and
flanks; tail thick and bushy

**Habits** Solitary creature that roams widely; mainly nocturnal in
summer

**Breeding** One litter of up to 4 babies born February–March after
gestation period of 30–40 days (including up to 9
months delayed implantation). Weaned at 8–10 weeks;
sexually mature at 2–3 years. May live up to 18 years in
captivity, 11 in the wild

**Voice** Hisses and growls when annoyed; also playful squeaks
and grunts

**Diet** Mostly rodents; sometimes larger mammals, especially as
carrion; also fruit, berries, birds, and eggs

**Habitat** Mountainous forests, rocky areas, and tundra in summer

**Distribution** Widely distributed across northern Europe and
Russia; also Canada and northern U.S.

**Status** Population: unknown, probably low thousands;
IUCN Vulnerable

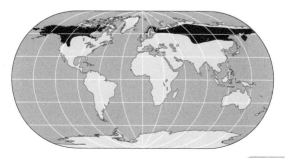

# European Otter

**Common name**
European otter

**Scientific name** *Lutra lutra*

**Family** Mustelidae

**Order** Carnivora

**Size** Length head/body: 24–35 in
(60–90 cm); tail length: 14–18.5 in (35–47 cm);
height at shoulder: about 6 in (15 cm). Male about 20%
bigger than female

**Weight** 13–37 lb (6–17 kg)

**Key features** Long, slender body with short legs and long,
tapering tail; light- or dark-brown fur with broad,
flattened head, small ears, and small eyes; all 4 feet
are webbed

**Habits** Lives alone; swims and dives well but can be active on
land; usually nocturnal, may come out during the day

**Breeding** Usually 2–3 cubs born after gestation period of 2
months; births at any time of year in western Europe,
more seasonal in the north and east. Weaned at 4
months; sexually mature at 1 year. May live up to 15
years in captivity, about 3–4 in the wild

**Voice** Occasional shrill whistle, otherwise silent

**Diet** Slow-swimming fish, especially eels, but also mussels,
shrimps, crabs, and lobsters

**Habitat** Edges of rivers and lakes, often in reed beds; rocky
coasts in some areas

**Distribution** From Britain throughout most of western Europe
east to China and Japan; also in south India, Sri Lanka,
Malaysia, Sumatra, and parts of North Africa

**Status** Population: widespread but scarce; IUCN Vulnerable;
CITES I. Declining in most areas; has become extinct in
parts of Europe in the last 50 years

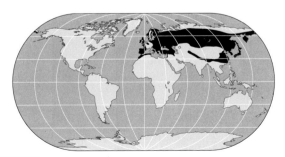

# North American River Otter

**Common name**
North American
river otter (northern river otter)

**Scientific name** *Lontra canadensis*

**Family** Mustelidae

**Order** Carnivora

**Size** Length head/body: 26–42 in (66–107 cm); tail length: 12–20 in (32–46 cm); height at shoulder: 10–12 in (25–30 cm). Male larger than female

**Weight** 11–31 lb (5–14 kg)

**Key features** Long, cylindrical body and short, stocky legs; long, pointed tail; small, blunt head with small ears and eyes; fur light to dark brown

**Habits** Lively, playful: lives alone or in small groups; semiaquatic; active at any time of day

**Breeding** Litters of 1–6 (usually 2 or 3) cubs born from November–May after approximately 50 days' gestation. Weaned at 5–6 months; sexually mature at 2 or 3 years. May live to 21 years in captivity, 14 in the wild

**Voice** Shrill chirps, soft "chuckles," grunts, coughs, and growls; loud screams when frightened

**Diet** Fish; also crayfish, frogs, birds' eggs, small mammals

**Habitat** Coastal and freshwater: rivers, streams, lakes, reservoirs, marshes, swamps, and estuaries

**Distribution** Canada and mainly northwestern, southeastern, and Great Lakes states of U.S.

**Status** Population: probably low thousands; CITES II. Common in parts of U.S. and Canada; extinct or rare in others

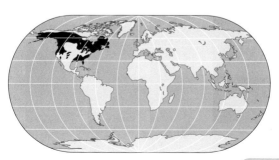

# Giant River Otter

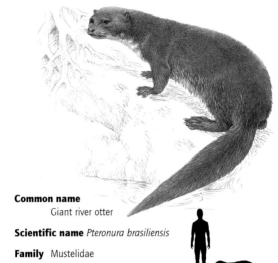

**Common name**
Giant river otter

**Scientific name** *Pteronura brasiliensis*

**Family** Mustelidae

**Order** Carnivora

**Size** Length head/body: 34-55 in (86-140 cm);
tail length: 13-39 in (33-100 cm); height at shoulder:
16 in (40 cm)

**Weight** Male 57-75 lb (26-34 kg); female 48-57 lb (22-26 kg)

**Key features** Large otter with short, glossy brown fur that looks
black when wet; often white or creamy nose and throat;
webbed feet; tail tapers and is flattened with a flange
along each edge

**Habits** Lives in family groups, mostly in the water

**Breeding** Up to 5 young born in a single litter each year after
gestation period of 65-70 days. Weaned at 3-4 months;
sexually mature at 2 years. May live over 14 years in
captivity, possibly similar in the wild

**Voice** Loud yelps, barks, and whistles; very vocal

**Diet** Mainly fish, but also freshwater crabs and occasional
mammals

**Habitat** Slow-moving rivers, creeks, and swamps, especially
within forested areas

**Distribution** Once over much of tropical South America south to
Argentina; now rare and patchy

**Status** Population: perhaps fewer than 2,000 left in the wild;
IUCN Endangered; CITES I

# Sea Otter

**Common name** Sea otter

**Scientific name** *Enhydra lutris*

**Family** Mustelidae

**Order** Carnivora

**Size** Length head/body: 29.5–35 in (75–90 cm); tail length: 11–12.5 in (28–32 cm); height at shoulder: 8–10 in (20–25 cm)

**Weight** 30–85 lb (14–38 kg)

**Key features** Dark-brown otter with blunt-looking head that turns pale cream with age; feet completely webbed; hind feet form flippers

**Habits** Floats on back in kelp beds and calm waters; dives to feed from seabed

**Breeding** One pup born each year in early summer after gestation period of 4 months (including up to 8 months delayed implantation). Weaned at 5 months; females sexually mature at 3 years; males at 5-6 years, but do not breed successfully until at least 7 years. May live for over 20 years in captivity, similar in the wild

**Voice** Normally silent

**Diet** Crabs, shellfish, sea urchins, fish; other marine animals

**Habitat** Kelp beds and rocky seashores

**Distribution** Formerly along coasts across eastern and northern Pacific from California to Kamchatka and northern Japan; exterminated over most of its range, now reintroduced to coasts of California, Alaska, Oregon, and Washington

**Status** Population: about 150,000 and growing; IUCN Endangered; CITES II. Given full legal protection in 1911 and probably now secure

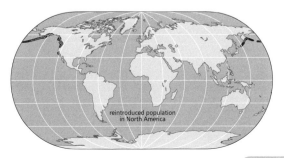

reintroduced population in North America

# American Badger

**Common name** American badger

**Scientific name** *Taxidea taxus*

**Family** Mustelidae

**Order** Carnivora

**Size** Length head/body: 16.5-28 in (42-72 cm); tail length: 4-6 in (10-15 cm); height at shoulder: 8-10 in (20-25 cm)

**Weight** Male 18-26.5 lb (8-12 kg); female 13-18 lb (6-8 kg)

**Key features** Flattened body with short legs, long curved foreclaws, and shovel-like hind claws; gray to yellowish-brown fur with cream belly; sides of face white; dark patches behind ears and on cheeks; white stripe from forehead to nose

**Habits** Forages at night; does not hibernate; solitary, except for breeding pairs and family groups

**Breeding** Litters of 1-5 young born late March or early April after gestation period of 7 months (including 5.5 months delayed implantation). Weaned at 6 weeks; female sexually mature at 12 months, male at 14 months. May live for 26 years in captivity, 12-14 in the wild

**Voice** Normally silent, but occasional yelps

**Diet** Mainly burrowing mammals such as pocket gophers and ground squirrels; also birds, reptiles, insects, and occasionally some plants

**Habitat** Treeless regions, prairies, meadows, and cold desert

**Distribution** Parts of Canada, U.S., and Mexico

**Status** Population: unknown, perhaps low thousands. Increasing, but still uncommon

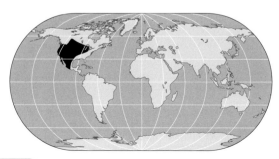

# European Badger

**Common name** European badger

**Scientific name** *Meles meles*

**Family** Mustelidae

**Order** Carnivora

**Size** Length head/body: 27.5–31 in (70–80 cm); tail length: 5–7 in (12–19 cm); height at shoulder: 12 in (30 cm)

**Weight** 18–26 lb (8–12 kg)

**Key features** Dog-sized animal with short legs and long, coarse hair, grizzled gray on back and black on belly; face is white with prominent black stripes running backward through the eyes

**Habits** Nocturnal; occupies a clan territory; often inactive for long periods in winter, but does not hibernate

**Breeding** Usually 1–4 cubs born around February after gestation period of 10–12 months (including 8–10 months delayed implantation). Weaned at about 4 months; sexually mature at 2 years. May live to be 16 years in captivity, 10 in the wild

**Voice** Occasional yelps and loud whickering noises

**Diet** Almost anything edible found at ground level, including worms, small mammals, roots, fruit, acorns, and beetles

**Habitat** Woodlands, farmlands, even suburban areas where there is access to food; prefers well-drained soils on slopes for burrowing

**Distribution** Widespread in most of Europe from Britain and Spain eastward to China and Japan

**Status** Population: probably at least 1.5 million. Generally scarce, even extinct in some areas, but increasingly common in parts of Britain

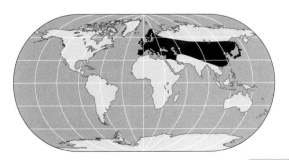

# Honey Badger

**Common name** Honey badger (ratel)

**Scientific name** *Mellivora capensis*

**Family** Mustelidae

**Order** Carnivora

**Size** Length head/body: 24–30 in (60–77 cm); tail length: 8–12 in (20–30 cm); height at shoulder: 10–12 in (25–30 cm)

**Weight** 15.5–28.5 lb (7–13 kg)

**Key features** Solidly built animal with short tail and short, sturdy legs with extremely long, strong claws; fur usually grizzled gray on back, black to brown elsewhere; head small with short muzzle and small eyes

**Habits** Nocturnal; excellent digger; usually solitary; extremely aggressive

**Breeding** One to 4 (usually 2) young born at any time of year after gestation period of 6 months. Weaning and sexual maturity unknown. May live up to 26 years in captivity, perhaps 10 in the wild

**Voice** Harsh growls when angry

**Diet** Mammals, reptiles, poisonous snakes, birds, insects, and worms; also carrion, eggs, fruit, and honey

**Habitat** Anywhere with suitable sites for dens—forests, grassy plains, and rocky slopes

**Distribution** Africa and southwestern Asia

**Status** Population: unknown, probably a few thousand. Widespread but declining

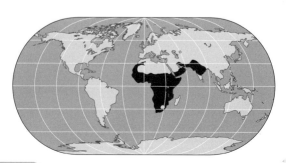

# Striped Skunk

**Common name** Striped skunk

**Scientific name** *Mephitis mephitis*

**Family** Mustelidae

**Order** Carnivora

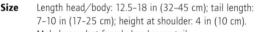

**Size** Length head/body: 12.5–18 in (32–45 cm); tail length: 7–10 in (17–25 cm); height at shoulder: 4 in (10 cm). Male larger, but female has longer tail

**Weight** 3–13 lb (1.5–6 kg)

**Key features** Cat-sized animal, with small head tapering to a bulbous nose; black coat with forked white stripes on back; white patch and stripe on head; long, bushy tail

**Habits** Mainly active at night and at dusk and dawn; generally solitary; squirts foul-smelling liquid when threatened; may swim if necessary

**Breeding** Three to 9 young born May–June after gestation period of 62–66 days (including delayed implantation). Weaned at 6–8 weeks; sexually mature at 1 year. May live 8–10 years in captivity, fewer than 3 in the wild

**Voice** Low growls, grunts, and snarls; also churring and short squeals; occasional screech or hiss

**Diet** Mainly insects; also small rodents, rabbits, birds, eggs, carrion, fruit, vegetables, and garbage

**Habitat** Forest or field edges, patches of brush, rocky outcrops, and wooded ravines; town gardens

**Distribution** Southern Canada, U.S., and northern Mexico

**Status** Population: abundant

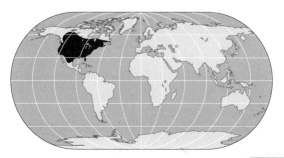

# Common Genet

**Common name**
Common genet
(European or small-spotted genet)

**Scientific name** *Genetta genetta*

**Family** Viverridae

**Order** Carnivora

**Size** Length head/body: 16–22 in
(40–55 cm); tail length: 16–20 in (40–50 cm);
height at shoulder: 7–8 in (18–20 cm)

**Weight** 3–5 lb (1.5–2 kg)

**Key features** Sandy coat with dark spots forming long stripes;
tail with dark rings and white tip; short, dark crest of
longer hair down spine

**Habits** Active during the night and twilight periods; solitary, but
tolerates others; climbs, jumps, and swims well

**Breeding** Litters of 1–4 young born after gestation period of 70
days. Breeding occurs year-round, but mainly April to
May and August to September. Weaned at 6 months;
sexually mature at 2 years. May live up to 20 years in
captivity, probably many fewer in the wild

**Voice** Normally silent, but will hiss, growl, purr, and mew; may
also cough, whine, or scream

**Diet** Mostly rodents, especially mice; also rabbits, birds,
lizards, fruit, berries, and insects

**Habitat** Dense scrub, woodland, and rocky areas; up to 6,500 ft
(2,000 m) in the Pyrenees

**Distribution** Europe (France and the Iberian Peninsula),
Palestine, and Africa (except for the Sahara Desert and
Congo River Basin)

**Status** Population: abundant; IUCN Vulnerable (Balearic Island
subspecies). Widespread and fairly common

# Common Palm Civet

**Common name**
Common palm civet (toddy cat)

**Scientific name** *Paradoxurus hermaphroditus*

**Family** Viverridae

**Order** Carnivora

**Size** Length head/body: 16.5–27.5 in (42–70 cm); tail length: 16–24 in (41–60 cm)

**Weight** 6–10 lb (2.7–4.5 kg)

**Key features** Sandy gray to dark-brown coat with black stripes down back; spots on shoulders, sides, and base of tail; face has mask of spots and a streak on the forehead; tail tip may be white

**Habits** Nocturnal; expert climber; spends much time in trees

**Breeding** Litters of 2–5 young born mainly between October and December after gestation period of 3 months. Weaned at 6 months; sexually mature at 11–12 months. May live up to 25 years in captivity, about 10 in the wild

**Voice** Normally silent

**Diet** Small vertebrates such as mice and lizards; also insects, fruit, and seeds

**Habitat** Forests and wooded areas; may shelter in thatched roofs and pipes

**Distribution** Kashmir, Indian Peninsula, and Sri Lanka to southeastern China and Malay Peninsula; also islands of Hainan (China), Sumatra, Sulawesi, Simeulue, Enggano, Kangean Islands, Java (Indonesia), Palawan (Philippines), Borneo, and many other nearby islands

**Status** Population: abundant; IUCN Vulnerable (subspecies *P. h. lignicolor*). A common animal

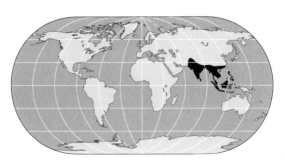

# Fossa

**Common name** Fossa

**Scientific name** *Cryptoprocta ferox*

**Family** Viverridae

**Order** Carnivora

**Size** Length head/body: 24–31 in (60–80 cm); tail length: 24–30 in (60–75 cm); height at shoulder: 14 in (35 cm)

**Weight** 15–26 lb (7–12 kg); occasionally up to 44 lb (20 kg)

**Key features** Reddish-brown to dark-brown coat, occasionally black; fur is short, thick, and smooth; catlike head with rounded ears; feet are webbed and have short, retractile claws

**Habits** Mainly nocturnal, but can be active in daylight; lives mostly in trees and is a skilled climber and powerful predator; solitary except during the breeding season

**Breeding** Litters of 2–4 young born after gestation period of 3 months. Weaned at 4–6 months; sexually mature at 4 years. May live to at least 20 years in captivity, probably fewer in the wild

**Voice** Generally silent

**Diet** Lemurs, small mammals, and birds; also reptiles, frogs, snakes, and insects

**Habitat** Rain forest and wooded savanna

**Distribution** Madagascar

**Status** Population: probably only a few hundred; IUCN Endangered; CITES II

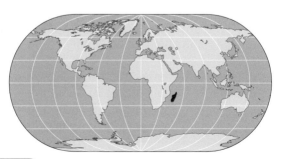

# Meerkat

**Common name** Meerkat (suricate, gray meerkat, slender-tailed meerkat)

**Scientific name** *Suricata suricatta*

**Family** Herpestidae

**Order** Carnivora

**Size** Length head/body: 12–18 in (30–45 cm); tail length: 6–12 in (15–30 cm); height at shoulder: 4 in (10 cm)

**Weight** 3.3–5 lb (1.5–2.3 kg)

**Key features** Slender, short-legged animal; tan to gray with broken brown bands on back and sides; black eye rings, ears, and tail tip

**Habits** Social: lives in colonies of up to 30, but usually 10–15, animals; sentries posted to watch for predators while colony is foraging

**Breeding** Two to 5 young born after gestation period of 75 days. Weaned at 9–10 weeks; sexually mature at about 12 months. May live 13 years in captivity, up to 10 in the wild, but more commonly 6

**Voice** A variety of chirrups, trills, growls, and barks

**Diet** Insects, scorpions, and grubs; occasionally lizards, small snakes, birds, and mice

**Habitat** Dry savanna, open plains, and scrubland

**Distribution** Southern Africa in Angola, Namibia, South Africa, and southern Botswana

**Status** Population: abundant. Not threatened, but numbers have fallen in some areas

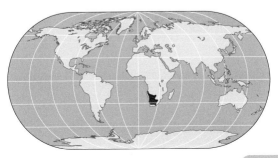

# Dwarf Mongoose

**Common name** Dwarf mongoose

**Scientific name** *Helogale parvula*

**Family** Herpestidae

**Order** Carnivora

**Size** Length head/body: 7–11 in (18–28 cm); tail length: 5.5–7.5 in (14–19 cm); height at shoulder: 5 in (12 cm)

**Weight** 8–13 oz (23–37 g). Male slightly smaller than female

**Key features** Small, slender mongoose with short legs; coat color ranges from grayish-tan to dark brown with fine gray speckles

**Habits** Active only during day; social: lives in packs of 2–20 (sometimes up to 40) individuals; searches for food in a group

**Breeding** Litters of up to 6 young born after a gestation period of about 53 days. Weaned at 6–7 weeks; sexually mature at about 3 years. May live up to about 12 years in captivity, 10 in the wild

**Voice** Vibrating chirrup; warning call is a shrill double note or shriek

**Diet** Invertebrates, particularly crickets, grasshoppers, termites, scorpions, and spiders; vertebrate prey includes mice, lizards, snakes, and birds; some fruit

**Habitat** Savannas, thickets, and woodlands, especially where there are numerous termite mounds

**Distribution** Africa from Ethiopia to northern South Africa and west to northern Namibia and Angola

**Status** Population: abundant. Not at risk

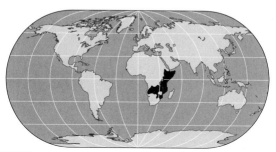

# Indian Gray Mongoose

**Common name** Indian gray mongoose
(Indian mongoose, common Indian mongoose,
common gray mongoose, common Bengal mongoose)

**Scientific name** *Herpestes edwardsii*

**Family** Herpestidae

**Order** Carnivora

**Size** Length head/body: 16–18 in
(40–45 cm); tail length:
16–18 in (40–45 cm); height at shoulder: up to 8 in
(20 cm)

**Weight** 2.2–4.5 lb (1–2 kg)

**Key features** Gray to light-brown coat, finely speckled with black

**Habits** Solitary; agile; good climber; hunts during the day

**Breeding** Litters of 2–4 young born after gestation period of 60
days. Weaned at about 1 month; sexually mature at 2
years. May live 20 years in captivity, 8–10 in the wild

**Voice** Angry chatters and chirrups

**Diet** Small mammals, birds, and lizards; some insects, snakes,
and eggs

**Habitat** Open country or thin woodland

**Distribution** From eastern and central Arabia to Nepal, India,
and Sri Lanka. Introduced to Malaysia, Mauritius, the
West Indies, Hawaii, and the Ryukyu and Tonaki islands
of Japan

**Status** Population: abundant. A common animal

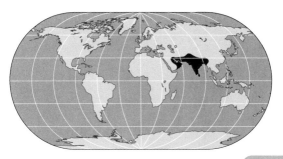

# Northern Fur Seal

**Common name** Northern fur seal

**Scientific name** *Callorhinus ursinus*

**Family** Otariidae

**Order** Pinnipedia

**Size** Length: male up to 6.5 ft (2 m); female 3.7–4.6 ft (1.1–1.4 m)

**Weight** Male 300–615 lb (136–279 kg); female 66–110 lb (30–50 kg)

**Key features** Large fur seal; bulls reddish-brown and black, cows pale and more gray

**Habits** Spends most of the year swimming and diving out at sea; comes ashore to breed in early summer in large colonies

**Breeding** One young born per year after gestation period of 12 months (including 4 months delayed implantation). Weaned at 3–4 months; females sexually mature at 4 years, males at 6 years but rarely breed before 10 years. May live more than 30 years in captivity, 26 in the wild

**Voice** Loud bellowing and barking

**Diet** Mainly fish

**Habitat** Open sea within 60 miles (100 km) of the coast; comes ashore only to breed

**Distribution** North Pacific coasts as far south as California; main breeding colonies occur on Pribilof and Commander Islands

**Status** Population: about 1 million; IUCN Vulnerable

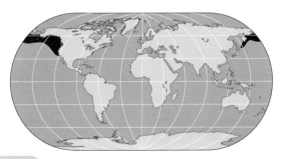

# Steller's Sea Lion

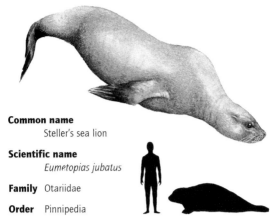

**Common name**
Steller's sea lion

**Scientific name**
*Eumetopias jubatus*

**Family** Otariidae

**Order** Pinnipedia

**Size** Length: male 9–10.5 ft (2.7–3.2 m);
female 7.5–9.5 ft (2.3–2.8 m)

**Weight** Male 1,980–3,970 lb (900–1,800 kg); female
580–770 lb (263–350 kg)

**Key features** Largest species of sea lion; fur appears golden
yellowish-brown when dry, dark-brown when wet

**Habits** Spends most of its time swimming and diving in coastal
waters, but comes ashore to breed and to rest and bask

**Breeding** Single pup born May–July after gestation period of
11.5 months (including 3–4 months delayed
implantation). Weaned at 12–24 months; sexually
mature at 4 years. Females may live over 30 years,
males rarely more than 15

**Voice** Loud barking and bellowing, especially on
breeding grounds

**Diet** Mostly fish, particularly pollock, but also salmon,
herring, mackerel, and sometimes squid and octopus

**Habitat** Rocky coasts and offshore islands; sea caves

**Distribution** North Pacific coasts from California to Japan

**Status** Population: probably fewer than 89,000; IUCN
Endangered. A species in decline

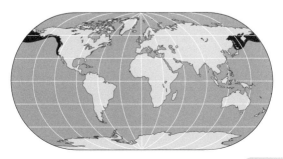

# California Sea Lion

**Common name** California sea lion

**Scientific name** *Zalophus californianus*

**Family** Otariidae

**Order** Pinnipedia

**Size** Length: male 7–8.6 ft (2–2.6 m); female 5–7 ft (1.5–2 m)

**Weight** Male 440–880 lb (200–400 kg); female 110–240 lb (50–110 kg)

**Key features** Long neck and hind flippers; bulls dark brown, females and young lighter, pups black; adult males have high, domed head, often paler than rest of body

**Habits** Forms large groups hauled out on rocky shores and on floating jetties in harbors

**Breeding** Single pup born May–July in California, less seasonal elsewhere, after gestation period of almost 1 year Weaned at 1 year; females sexually mature at 6–8 years, males at 9 years. May live up to 34 years in captivity, probably fewer in the wild

**Voice** Loud barking and bellowing

**Diet** Fish, especially mackerel and anchovy

**Habitat** Cool seas along rocky coasts

**Distribution** California to British Columbia (*Z. c. californicus*), around Galápagos Islands (*Z. c. wollebaeki*), and off Japan and Korea (*Z. c. japonicus*)

**Status** Population: about 200,000 off California; up to 50,000 in Galápagos; IUCN Vulnerable (Galápagos population). Japanese population probably extinct

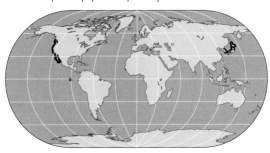

# Walrus

**Common name** Walrus

**Scientific name** *Odobenus rosmarus*

**Family** Odobenidae

**Order** Pinnipedia

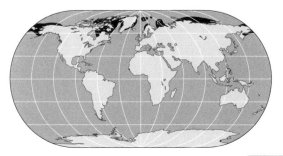

**Size** Length: male 8.8–11.5 ft (2.7–3.5 m); female 7.4–10.2 ft (2.3–3.1 m)

**Weight** Male 1,760–3,750 lb (800–1,700 kg); female 880–2,750 lb (400–1,247 kg)

**Key features** Vast, ponderous seal; generally pale brown all over; broad, deep snout bears 2 long tusks

**Habits** Feeds by diving in shallow seas; spends much time hauled out on shore, generally with other walruses

**Breeding** Single pup born April–June every 2 years after gestation period of more than 1 year. Weaned at up to 2 years; females sexually mature at 6–7 years, males at 8–10 years. May live over 40 years in the wild

**Voice** Bellowing and grunts; sometimes whistles

**Diet** Mollusks, crabs, worms, and invertebrates taken from seabed; occasionally fish

**Habitat** Arctic waters along edge of pack ice

**Distribution** Arctic Ocean: Pacific population along coasts of Siberia and Alaska, Atlantic population mainly around northern Canada, Greenland, and parts of Arctic Scandinavia

**Status** Population: at least 200,000 (Pacific); about 30–35,000 (Atlantic)

# Hawaiian Monk Seal

**Common name** Hawaiian monk seal

**Scientific name** *Monachus schauinslandi*

**Family** Phocidae

**Order** Pinnipedia

**Size** Length: 6.5–8.2 ft (2–2.5 m). Female about 10% longer than male

**Weight** 330–660 lb (150–300 kg). Female heavier than male

**Key features** Completely tropical seal, but with no obvious anatomical adaptations to warm climate; adult coat silvery gray on back with cream belly, throat, and chest; turns brown and yellow as seal ages; sometimes has a red or green tinge from algal growth on fur; pups born with a black coat, lost at about 6 weeks

**Habits** Adults usually solitary; groups sometimes form on beaches, but for favorable conditions rather than as form of gregarious behavior; feeds at night, spends majority of the day resting on beaches; may disperse throughout range, but not migratory

**Breeding** Single pup born after gestation period of 11–12 months. Weaned at 40 days; females sexually mature at 4–8 years, males unknown. May live 25–30 years

**Voice** Males roar in breeding season

**Diet** Reef-dwelling invertebrates and fish, including lobsters, eels, flatfish, and octopus

**Habitat** Sandy, tropical beaches and shallow lagoons

**Distribution** Found on islands northwest of Hawaii

**Status** Population: 1,200–1,500; IUCN Endangered; CITES I

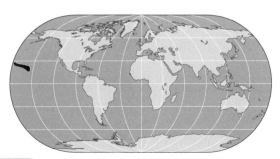

# Northern Elephant Seal

**Common name** Northern elephant seal

**Scientific name** *Mirounga angustirostris*

**Family** Phocidae

**Order** Pinnipedia

**Size** Length: male 13–16.5 ft (4–5 m); female 6.5–10 ft (2–3 m)

**Weight** Male 2–3 tons (1.8–2.7 tonnes); female 1,300–2,000 lb (600–900 kg)

**Key features** Huge seal with bent, floppy nose; unlike almost all other seals, brown all over

**Habits** Spends most of its time at sea; occasionally hauls out to rest on rocky islands and beaches

**Breeding** Single pup born after gestation period of 11 months (including 2–3 months delayed implantation). Weaned at 4 weeks; females sexually mature at about 5 years, males at 8–9 years. May live up to 20 years, but males usually fewer than 12

**Voice** Bellows and roars

**Diet** Mostly squid caught in midwater; also some small sharks and slow-moving fish

**Habitat** Cold coastal waters

**Distribution** North Pacific coasts of North America from California to northern Mexico

**Status** Population: about 100,000–150,000

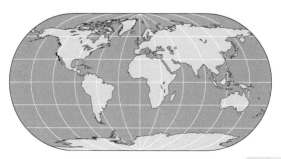

# Crabeater Seal

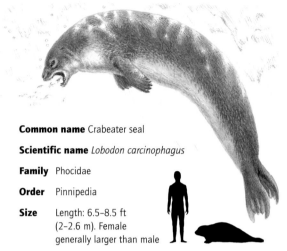

**Common name** Crabeater seal

**Scientific name** *Lobodon carcinophagus*

**Family** Phocidae

**Order** Pinnipedia

**Size** Length: 6.5–8.5 ft (2–2.6 m). Female generally larger than male

**Weight** 440–660 lb (200–300 kg)

**Key features** Slim seal; silvery gray in color with variable brown ring markings on sides; coat fades to white in summer; long snout; specially ridged teeth in cheeks; no external ears; often scarred from attacks by leopard seals and fights with other crabeaters

**Habits** Male joins female after she has given birth; when pup is weaned, male mates with female, and family group disbands; crabeaters are usually solitary or found in small groups, but larger aggregations can occur

**Breeding** Single calf born after gestation period of 11 months, probably including period of delayed implantation. Weaned at 14–21 days; sexually mature at 3–6 years, often depending on food availability. May live up to 40 years, but average is about 20

**Voice** Snorts, hisses, and blows through nose when frightened; deep groaning sounds produced while underwater

**Diet** Krill, other invertebrates, and small fish

**Habitat** Stays close to the pack ice of the Antarctic

**Distribution** Circumpolar, following the advancing and retreating pack ice of Antarctica

**Status** Population: may be over 10 million. The world's most abundant seal

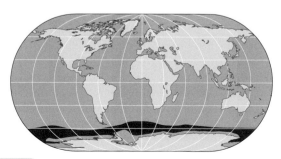

# Leopard Seal

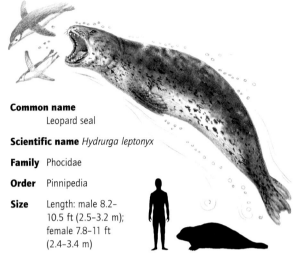

**Common name**
Leopard seal

**Scientific name** *Hydrurga leptonyx*

**Family** Phocidae

**Order** Pinnipedia

**Size** Length: male 8.2–10.5 ft (2.5–3.2 m); female 7.8–11 ft (2.4–3.4 m)

**Weight** Male 440–990 lb (200–450 kg); female 495–1,300 lb (225–590 kg)

**Key features** Large, slender seal with reptilelike head that is more distinct from body than most seals; powerful jaws with wide gape; long canines and sharply pointed molars; long, broad front flippers; dark-gray back, paler sides and silvery underside; variable spots on shoulders, throat, sides, and stomach

**Habits** Solitary, ferocious creatures; segregated by age to different areas; often found near penguin and seal colonies

**Breeding** Single pup born after gestation period of 11 months (including a probable 2-month period of delayed implantation). Weaned at about 4 weeks; females sexually mature at 3 years, males at 4 years. May live at least 26 years in the wild, rarely kept in captivity

**Voice** Gargling, grunting, whistling, and birdlike chirps; low droning sound made underwater

**Diet** Krill and other crustaceans; penguins, seals, and squid

**Habitat** Antarctic and subantarctic waters, often near pack ice

**Distribution** Circumpolar distribution along edges of antarctic pack ice; found all year round and seasonally on subantarctic islands; sometimes along Australian and South African coasts

**Status** Population: unknown. Generally abundant

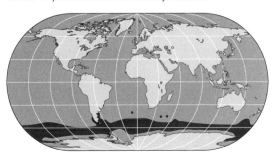

# Harbor Seal

**Common name** Harbor seal (common seal)

**Scientific name** *Phoca vitulina*

**Family** Phocidae

**Order** Pinnipedia

**Size** Length: 47–79 in
(120–200 cm).
Male up to 30% larger than female

**Weight** 100–285 lb (45–130 kg)

**Key features** Typical medium-sized seal; pale-cream coat
blotched with mottled pattern of gray, brown, or black;
often looks silvery when dry; head small and rounded
with short, narrow muzzle

**Habits** Basks on rocks and sandbanks, usually in small groups;
feeds at sea by making short dives

**Breeding** Single pup born in June and July after gestation period
of 10.5–11 months (including 2–3 months delayed
implantation). Weaned at 3–6 weeks; females sexually
mature at 2 years, males at 5 years. Females may live up
to 32 years in the wild, males up to 26 years; probably
fewer in captivity

**Voice** Short barks and grunts, but probably the least vocal
of seals

**Diet** Mainly fish caught on or near the seabed

**Habitat** Rocky and sandy coasts, estuaries, and sheltered inlets

**Distribution** Coasts of North Pacific and North Atlantic

**Status** Population: probably well over half a million. Common
and widespread

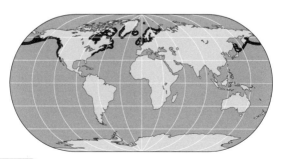

# Gray Seal

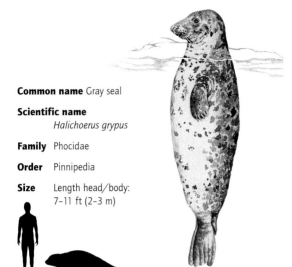

**Common name** Gray seal

**Scientific name**
  *Halichoerus grypus*

**Family**  Phocidae

**Order**  Pinnipedia

**Size**  Length head/body:
  7–11 ft (2–3 m)

**Weight**  Male 375–680 lb (170–308 kg); female 230–410 lb
  (104–186 kg)

**Key features**  Big, dark-gray seal with pale blotches; top of head
  forms flat profile; snout broad and conical in bull

**Habits**  Spends most of year out at sea, but comes ashore to rest
  and breed; dives to catch food

**Breeding**  Single calf born after gestation period of 11.5 months
  (including 3 months delayed implantation). Weaned at 3
  weeks; females sexually mature at 4–5 years, males at
  6–8 years. Females may live over 40 years, males many
  fewer, about 15–20 years

**Voice**  Loud barking sounds

**Diet**  Fish, especially cod and salmon; occasionally octopus

**Habitat**  Rocky coasts with sandy beaches; open sea

**Distribution**  Coasts of Britain, Scandinavia, Iceland, and Baltic;
  off Labrador and Nova Scotia (Canada), occasionally
  south as far as New Jersey

**Status**  Population: about 200,000; IUCN Endangered
  (Baltic population)

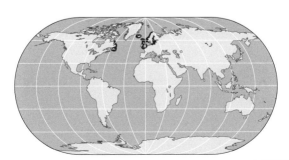

# Harp Seal

**Common name** Harp seal (saddleback seal)

**Scientific name** *Phoca (Pagophilus) groenlandica*

**Family** Phocidae

**Order** Pinnipedia

**Size** Length: 5.6–6.4 ft (1.7–2 m)

**Weight** 250–310 lb (113–141 kg)

**Key features** Adults light gray with a black face and bold, curved dark marking on the back; pups white

**Habits** Spends most of year at sea along edges of Arctic ice

**Breeding** Single pup born in February after gestation period of 10 months (including 4 months delayed implantation). Weaned at 10–12 days; sexually mature at about 5.5 years, but often does not breed until about 8 years. May live up to 30 years

**Voice** Various barks, grunts, and growls; 15 different vocalizations recorded

**Diet** Shrimp and small fish, especially capelin

**Habitat** Open seas and edges of ice floes

**Distribution** Populations based on 3 breeding areas: Newfoundland, Jan Mayen Island, and White Sea, with animals dispersing and going farther north in summer

**Status** Population: probably at least 3 million. Abundant

# Amazon Dolphin

**Common name** Amazon dolphin (boto, pink dolphin)

**Scientific name** *Inia geoffrensis*

**Family** Iniidae

**Order** Cetacea

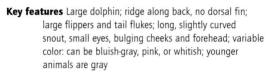

**Size** Length: male 6.5–9 ft (2–2.7 m); female 5–7.5 ft (1.5–2.3 m)

**Weight** 190–285 lb (86–129 kg)

**Key features** Large dolphin; ridge along back, no dorsal fin; large flippers and tail flukes; long, slightly curved snout, small eyes, bulging cheeks and forehead; variable color: can be bluish-gray, pink, or whitish; younger animals are gray

**Habits** Lives alone, in pairs, or occasionally small groups; most active in early morning or late afternoon; slow swimmer, often swimming on side or upside down; sometimes jumps up to 40 in (100 cm) into air; occasionally puts whole head out of water, but mostly just forehead and blowhole; makes short dives of 30–40 seconds

**Breeding** Single calf born May–September after gestation period of 10–11 months. Weaned at 1 year or more; probably sexually mature at about 8 years. May live at least 20 years in captivity, up to 30 in the wild

**Voice** Breathes out in long, slow sigh; spray sometimes reaches 6 ft (1.8 m)

**Diet** Mostly fish; some crustaceans, including crabs; also small turtles

**Habitat** Rivers and flooded forests

**Distribution** South America in Amazon and Orinoco river systems

**Status** Population: unknown, probably a few thousand; IUCN Vulnerable; CITES II. Threatened and becoming scarce

# Killer Whale

**Common name**
Killer whale (orca)

**Scientific name** *Orcinus orca*

**Family** Delphinidae

**Order** Cetacea

**Size** Length: male 17–29.5 ft (5.2–9 m);
female 15–25.5 ft (4.5–7.7 m)

**Weight** 3–10 tons (2.5–9 tonnes)

**Key features** Striking black-and-white markings;
body mainly black with white patch
behind eye, white cheeks and belly, and gray saddle
patch; head rounded with no obvious snout; tall,
triangular dorsal fin, up to 6 ft (1.8 m) high in male;
broad, rounded flippers; tail black on top, white on
underside

**Habits** Social, living in a tight-knit family group or "pod"; fast,
active swimmer; acrobatic at the surface, will breach,
spy-hop, and tail slap

**Breeding** Single calf born about every 8 years after gestation
period of 17 months. Weaned at 14–18 months; sexually
mature at 12–16 years. Males may live 35–60 years,
females up to 90 years in the wild; rarely survives more
than a few years in captivity

**Voice** Varied, including complex, often pulsed, calls

**Diet** Small fish and squid to seals, turtles, seabirds, and even
other whales

**Habitat** Open sea to coastal waters; estuaries; often around ice
floes in polar waters

**Distribution** Every ocean in the world, from polar regions to
equator

**Status** Population: 100,000; IUCN Lower Risk: conservation
dependent; CITES II. Widespread and quite numerous

# Long-Finned Pilot Whale

**Common name** Long-finned pilot whale

**Scientific name** *Globicephala melas*

**Family** Delphinidae

**Order** Cetacea

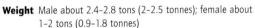

**Size** Length: male 13–25 ft (4–7.6 m); female 10–18.5 ft (3–5.6 m)

**Weight** Male about 2.4–2.8 tons (2–2.5 tonnes); female about 1–2 tons (0.9–1.8 tonnes)

**Key features** Medium-sized dolphin; black, dark-brown, or gray-black, sometimes with gray markings behind eye, on chin, and behind dorsal fin; rounded head with bulging forehead; dorsal fin wide, thick, curved back, and set toward front of body; flippers long and pointed

**Habits** Highly social: swims slowly in large groups; often seen lying horizontally in water apparently asleep; rarely leaps from water, but lifts tail above surface

**Breeding** One calf born per year after gestation period of 15 months. Weaned at 2 years; sexually mature at 8 years. May live over 60 years

**Voice** Clicks and whistles

**Diet** Mainly squid; some shoaling fish

**Habitat** Offshore, prefers deep water; occasionally comes into coastal or shallow waters to feed

**Distribution** North Atlantic and all waters of all seas in Southern Hemisphere

**Status** Widespread and fairly common

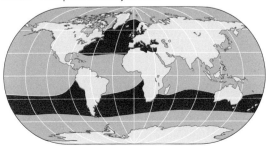

# Common Dolphin

**Common name** Common dolphin

**Scientific name** *Delphinus delphis*

**Family** Delphinidae

**Order** Cetacea

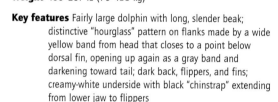

**Size** Length: 5–6.5 ft (1.5–2 m). Male generally larger than female

**Weight** 155–297 lb (70–135 kg)

**Key features** Fairly large dolphin with long, slender beak; distinctive "hourglass" pattern on flanks made by a wide yellow band from head that closes to a point below dorsal fin, opening up again as a gray band and darkening toward tail; dark back, flippers, and fins; creamy-white underside with black "chinstrap" extending from lower jaw to flippers

**Habits** Active, acrobatic, and noisy dolphin; fast swimming; sociable: normally found in groups of usually a few dozen animals

**Breeding** Single calf born every 1–2 years after gestation period of 10 months. Weaned at 12–18 months; sexually mature at 5–6 years. May live about 25 years in the wild, rarely kept in captivity

**Voice** Pulsed whistles, clicks, and high-pitched squeaks

**Diet** Squid and shoaling fish

**Habitat** Waters with a surface temperature of above 50°F (10°C), usually more than 600 ft (180 m) deep

**Distribution** Widespread in warm-temperate, tropical, and subtropical waters

**Status** Population: abundant, many millions; CITES II. Intensive hunting in Black Sea has reduced local population. Pacific population has suffered as a result of being accidentally caught by tuna fisheries

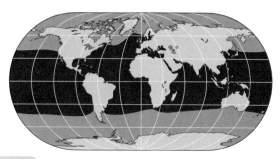

# Pacific White-Sided Dolphin

**Common name** Pacific white-sided dolphin

**Scientific name** *Lagenorhynchus obliquidens*

**Family** Delphinidae

**Order** Cetacea

**Size** Length: 5.6–7.8 ft (1.7–2.4 m)

**Weight** 187–330 lb (85–150 kg)

**Key features** Stocky dolphin with a short, almost invisible snout ("beak") and rounded, backward-curving dorsal fin; black or dark-gray back; thin gray stripe running along both sides from head and curving down toward tail, where it opens to a wide flank patch; gray patch on each side above flippers; fins dark at front fading to paler at rear; belly white

**Habits** Highly sociable dolphin, usually seen in large groups occasionally numbering thousands; lively and acrobatic; curious, often coming close to inspect boats

**Breeding** Single calf born every 2–3 years after gestation period of about 10–12 months. Weaned at 18 months; sexually mature at 10 years, sometimes more. May live up to 20 years in captivity, 45 in the wild

**Voice** Clicks and whistles

**Diet** Squid and small shoaling fish

**Habitat** Mainly offshore waters; occasionally seen inshore if water is deep

**Distribution** Cool-temperate waters of the North Pacific

**Status** Population: 1 million; CITES II. Common throughout most of its range

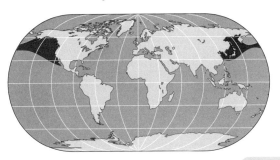

# Bottlenose Dolphin

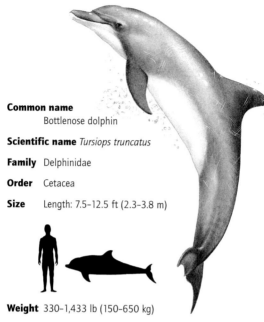

**Common name**
 Bottlenose dolphin

**Scientific name** *Tursiops truncatus*

**Family** Delphinidae

**Order** Cetacea

**Size** Length: 7.5–12.5 ft (2.3–3.8 m)

**Weight** 330–1,433 lb (150–650 kg)

**Key features** Robust dolphin with a wide head and body and rounded forehead; body mostly gray with a lighter or white underside; color patterns are variable

**Habits** Active, social dolphin usually seen in groups

**Breeding** Single calf born every 4–5 years after gestation period of 1 year. Weaned at 4–5 years; females sexually mature at 5–12 years, males at 10–12 years. May live up to 50 years in the wild, fewer in captivity

**Voice** High-pitched whistles and clicks

**Diet** Large variety of food, including fish, squid, octopus, cuttlefish, and mollusks

**Habitat** Wide range of habitats from open water to harbors, bays, lagoons, estuaries, and rocky reefs

**Distribution** Widespread in temperate and tropical waters

**Status** Population: unknown, perhaps hundreds of thousands of individuals; CITES II. A common species, especially in particular areas

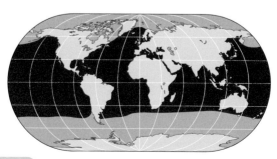

# Spinner Dolphin

**Common name** Spinner dolphin

**Scientific name** *Stenella longirostris*

**Family** Delphinidae

**Order** Cetacea

**Size** Length: 5.5–8 ft (1.7–2.4 m); Southeast Asian animals are smaller: about 4.5 ft (1.4 m) long

**Weight** 100–165 lb (45–75 kg); Southeast Asian animals: adults about 48 lb (22 kg)

**Key features** Slender body; long, thin snout ("beak"); 3-toned coloring: dark on top fading to gray, with a light belly

**Habits** Active, fast-swimming dolphin; often swims with boats for long periods of time; performs characteristic leaps, spinning up to 7 times; swims in groups of usually about 30 animals

**Breeding** Single calf born about every 3 years after gestation period of 10.5 months. Weaned at 1–2 years; females sexually mature at 4–7 years, males at 7–10 years. May live up to about 50 years

**Voice** Clicks and whistles

**Diet** Fish and squid

**Habitat** Mainly open ocean, but sometimes inshore

**Distribution** Tropical and subtropical seas throughout world

**Status** Population: several million; IUCN Lower Risk: conservation dependent; CITES II. Populations in the eastern Pacific are severely reduced from deaths associated with tuna fisheries

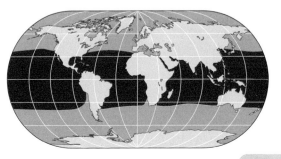

# Harbor Porpoise

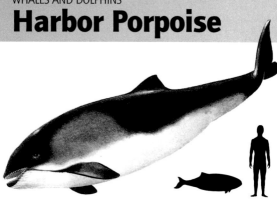

**Common name** Harbor porpoise (common porpoise)

**Scientific name** *Phocoena phocoena*

**Family** Phocoenidae

**Order** Cetacea

**Size** Length: 5–6 ft (1.5–1.9 m)

**Weight** 108–198 lb (49–90 kg)

**Key features** Small and blunt nosed; dark back, fading to pale belly; low dorsal fin and small flippers

**Habits** Forms small groups, typically of 2–5 animals; swims with a slow, rolling motion; keeps low in the water; rarely leaps; wary of boats

**Breeding** Single calf usually born each summer after gestation period of 11 months. Weaned at about 8 months; males sexually mature at 3–5 years, females slightly earlier, depending on region. May live up to 13 years

**Voice** Low-pitched calls; echolocation clicks up to 1,000 times per second; breathes with a "popping" or sneezing sound

**Diet** Mainly fish; occasionally squid and shrimp

**Habitat** Cool, shallow coastal waters, usually less than 330 ft (100 m) deep and cooler than 65°F (15°C); bays and estuaries, also offshore over sand banks

**Distribution** Temperate and subarctic waters of the Northern Hemisphere

**Status** Population: 200,000–300,000; IUCN Vulnerable; CITES II. Decreasing, mainly due to accidental capture in fishing nets, but also problems with disturbance, food supply, and disease

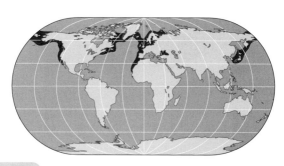

# Beluga

**Common name** Beluga (white whale)

**Scientific name** *Delphinapterus leucas*

**Family** Monodontidae

**Order** Cetacea

**Size** Length: 10–16 ft (3–5 m). Male larger than female

**Weight** 1,100–3,300 lb (500–1,500 kg)

**Key features** Stocky, white-colored whale; no dorsal fin; head small and rounded; flippers broad, short, paddle shaped, and highly mobile; tail fluke frequently asymmetrical

**Habits** Social animals, rarely seen alone; masculine groups of 3–15, nursery groups of mature females and several young of various ages; during migrations congregations of hundreds or even thousands may be seen

**Breeding** One calf born every 3 years after gestation period of 14–14.5 months. Weaned at 20–24 months; females sexually mature at 5 years, males at 8 years. May live 30–40 years in the wild, some have been known to live to 50 years; does not survive so long in captivity

**Voice** Trills, moos, clicks, squeaks, and twitters; sometimes called "sea canary"

**Diet** Mostly bottom feeders, eating fish, crustaceans, worms, and mollusks

**Habitat** Coastal and offshore in cold waters, usually near ice; shallow waters, rivers, and estuaries

**Distribution** Coasts of Arctic regions of North America, Greenland, northern Russia, and Svalbard

**Status** Population: about 100,000; IUCN Vulnerable; CITES II

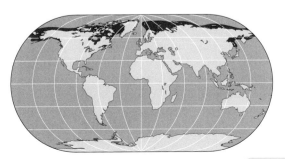

# Narwhal

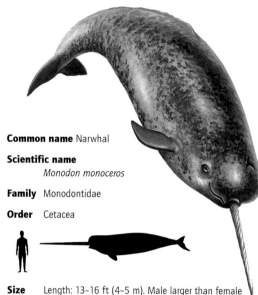

**Common name** Narwhal

**Scientific name**
Monodon monoceros

**Family** Monodontidae

**Order** Cetacea

**Size** Length: 13–16 ft (4–5 m). Male larger than female

**Weight** 1,760–3,520 lb (800–1,600 kg)

**Key features** Stocky toothed whale with no dorsal fin and short flippers; skin colored with patches of gray-green, cream, and black; males have unique long, spiral tusk

**Habits** Social: usually seen in groups of up to 20 animals; sometimes separate groups according to age and sex; often moves together as part of a much larger herd containing thousands of individuals

**Breeding** One calf born every 3 years after gestation period of 14–15 months. Weaned at 20 months; sexually mature at 6–8 years. May live 30–40 years

**Voice** Clicks, squeals, and whistles used for communication or navigation

**Diet** Mostly fish, squid, and shrimp

**Habitat** Cold Arctic seas, generally near sea ice; in summer sometimes seen in estuaries, deep fjords, and bays; migrates when habitat is unfavorable

**Distribution** Coastal; mainly western Greenland to mideastern Canada

**Status** Population: about 25,000–30,000; IUCN Data Deficient; CITES II. One of the less abundant whales, status uncertain

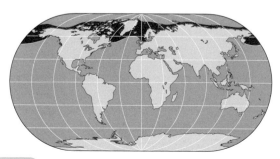

# Sperm Whale

**Common name**
Sperm whale

**Scientific name**
*Physeter catodon*

**Family** Physeteridae

**Order** Cetacea

**Size** Length: male 49–62 ft (15–19 m);
female 26–39 ft (8–12 m)

**Weight** Male 51 tons (45 tonnes),
maximum 65 tons (57 tonnes); female
17 tons (15 tonnes), maximum 27 tons (24 tonnes)

**Key features** Largest
toothed
whale; dark-
gray to dark-
brown skin
with white patches on belly; skin has a wrinkled
appearance; often scarred; large, square-ended head;
dorsal fin reduced to a small, triangular hump; short,
paddle-shaped flippers

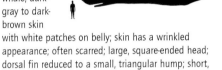

**Habits** Females and young live in breeding schools, young
males in bachelor schools, both with 20–25 individuals;
older males solitary or in small groups; join breeding
schools to mate

**Breeding** Single calf born every 4–6 years after gestation period
of 14–16 months. Weaned at 1–3 years, sometimes
longer; females sexually mature at 7–13 years, males at
18–21 years. May live at least 60–70 years

**Voice** Clicks used for communication and echolocation

**Diet** Mostly squid; also cuttle, octopus, and fish

**Habitat** Deep waters, often near the continental shelf; females
and calves stay in warm waters, males migrate to colder
feeding grounds

**Distribution** Found in all the oceans of the world

**Status** Population: estimates vary from 200,000 (minimum) to
1.5 million (maximum); IUCN Vulnerable; CITES I

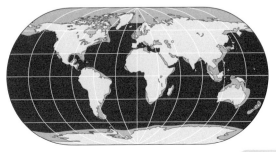

# Northern Bottlenose Whale

**Common name** Northern bottlenose whale

**Scientific name** *Hyperoodon ampullatus*

**Family** Ziphiidae

**Order** Cetacea

**Size** Length: 23–30 ft (7–9 m). Male larger than female

**Weight** Male 8 tons (7.5 tonnes); female 6.6 tons (5.8 tonnes)

**Key features** Medium-sized whale with distinctive, bulbous forehead and narrow snout ("beak"); lower jaw of beak extends slightly further than upper; 2 main teeth at tip of lower jaw in males; dorsal (back or spinal) regions dark gray to brown, lighter on belly; no notch in flukes (tail fin)

**Habits** Usually lives in groups of 1–4; larger herds formed when migrating and in the breeding season; older males often travel alone

**Breeding** One calf born every 2–3 years after gestation period of about a year. Weaned at about 12 months; females sexually mature at 8–12 years, males at about 7–9 years. May live approximately 30–40 years

**Voice** Little known, but uses clicks and whistles

**Diet** Mainly squid; also fish, sea cucumbers, cuttle, starfish, and prawns

**Habitat** Cold-temperate and Arctic waters, preferring offshore areas with water depths of over 3,300 ft (1,000 m)

**Distribution** North Atlantic oceans and Arctic regions, avoiding shallow waters

**Status** Population: probably a few thousand; IUCN Lower Risk: conservation dependent; CITES II. Insufficiently known; has declined due to hunting

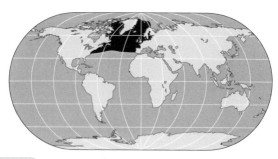

# Gray Whale

**Common name** Gray whale

**Scientific name** *Eschrichtius robustus*

**Family** Eschrichtiidae

**Order** Cetacea

**Size** Length: male
39-46 ft (12-14 m); female 43-49 ft (13-15 m)

**Weight** 26-40 tons (22.5-35 tonnes)

**Key features** Robust baleen whale; fairly short, upwardly curved
head; skin mottled gray, covered with patches of
barnacles and whale lice; no dorsal fin, but low hump
followed by series of bumps running to the large tail
flukes; flippers small and paddle shaped

**Habits** Generally found in small groups of 1-3, but larger
groups of up to 16 sometimes seen; large gatherings
form at feeding and breeding grounds; performs one of
the longest migrations of any mammal

**Breeding** Single calf born about every 2 years after gestation
period of 12-13 months. Weaned at 7-8 months;
sexually mature at between 5 and 11 years. May live
50-60 years, maximum documented 77 years

**Voice** Rumbles, groans, whistles, rasps, chirps, moans, growls,
and bongs

**Diet** Small invertebrates scooped off the seabed, including
crustaceans, mollusks, and worms

**Habitat** Shallow, coastal waters

**Distribution** Pacific Ocean; main population migrates between
summer feeding grounds north of Alaska in Chukchi and
Bering seas and winter breeding grounds off Baja
California; smaller population found off Korea and
Japan, but this group is close to extinction

**Status** Population: 20-25,000; IUCN Lower Risk: conservation
dependent; Critically Endangered (northwestern Pacific
stock); CITES I. Fairly common off western U.S.

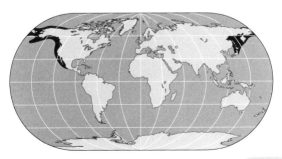

# Blue Whale

**Common name** Blue whale

**Scientific name** *Balaenoptera musculus*

**Family** Balaenopteridae

**Order** Cetacea

**Size** Length:
80–100 ft
(24–30 m).
Female generally larger than male

**Weight** 114–136 tons (100–120 tonnes), occasionally
up to 216 tons (190 tonnes)

**Key features** Long, streamlined rorqual whale—largest animal
on earth; blue-gray with pale mottling; ridge runs along
top of flat, "U"-shaped head; 2 blowholes with fleshy
splashguard; tapered flippers up to one-seventh of body
length; small, stubby dorsal fin; tail flukes broad and
triangular

**Habits** Shy and wary; mother and calf travel together, otherwise
tends to be solitary; sometimes larger numbers found
close together feeding or migrating; may associate with
fin whales

**Breeding** Single calf born after gestation period of 10–11
months. Weaned at 7–8 months; sexually mature at 5
years in females and just under 5 years in males. May
live 80–100 years

**Voice** Loud, low rumbling calls that travel long distances
under the water

**Diet** Principally krill, but also other small crustaceans and fish

**Habitat** Mainly open ocean, but will come closer to shore to
feed or breed; migrates between polar feeding grounds
and warmer subtropical and tropical breeding grounds

**Distribution** Found in all oceans of the world

**Status** Population: 3,500; IUCN Endangered; CITES I

# Humpback Whale

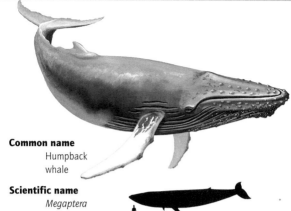

**Common name**
Humpback whale

**Scientific name**
*Megaptera novaeangliae*

**Family** Balaenopteridae

**Order** Cetacea

**Size** Length: male 38–50 ft (11.5–15 m). Male generally slightly smaller than female

**Weight** About 34 tons (30 tonnes); up to 55 tons (48 tonnes)

**Key features** Large, stocky baleen whale; upper body black or blue-black, underside white; long flippers; head and front edge of flippers have raised lumps called tubercles; tail flukes different in every individual

**Habits** More social than other rorqual whales, rarely seen alone; congregates in large groups to feed and breed; moves individually or in small parties of 2–3 within groups

**Breeding** One calf usually produced every 2 years after gestation period of 11–12 months. Weaned at 11 months; sexually mature at 4–6 years. May live 40–50 years, occasionally over 70

**Voice** Complex underwater songs consisting of grunts, groans, rasps, twitters, and moos

**Diet** Seasonal feeders on krill (shrimplike crustaceans) and small fish

**Habitat** Oceanic; enters shallower tropical waters in winter for breeding

**Distribution** Widely distributed; occurs seasonally in all oceans and from the Arctic to Antarctic

**Status** Population 30,000; IUCN Vulnerable; CITES I. Uncommon and threatened

# Minke Whale

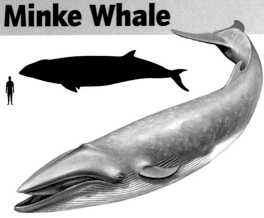

**Common name** Minke whale

**Scientific name** *Balaenoptera acutorostrata*

**Family** Balaenopteridae

**Order** Cetacea

**Size** Length: 23-33 ft (7-10 m). Female larger than male

**Weight** 7-11 tons (6-10 tonnes)

**Key features** Smallest and most abundant of the rorqual whales; black or dark gray in color with white belly; top of head appears flat with a raised central ridge and distinctive pointed snout; relatively short flippers, often with white band near base; tall dorsal fin

**Habits** Solitary or found in groups of 2 or 3; sometimes larger groups formed when feeding; can be quite inquisitive

**Breeding** One calf born every 2 years after gestation period of about 10 months. Weaned at 4-5 months; sexually mature at 6-7 years. May live up to 60 years

**Voice** Some grunts, clicks, thumps, and pings

**Diet** Filter feeders; mainly krill (planktonic shrimp) and fish, but will eat squid and types of plankton other than their favorite krill

**Habitat** Coastal and offshore polar, temperate, and tropical waters; seems to prefer cooler regions, but sometimes migrates

**Distribution** Widely distributed throughout all the oceans of the world

**Status** Population: 500,000-1 million; IUCN Lower Risk: near threatened; CITES I

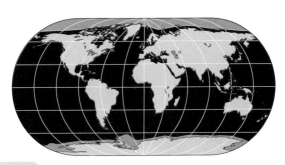

# Southern Right Whale

**Common name**
Southern
right whale

**Scientific name**
*Eubalaena australis*

**Family**  Balaenidae

**Order**  Cetacea

**Size**  Length: 46–59 ft (14–18 m). Female larger than male

**Weight**  57–64 tons (50–56 tonnes)

**Key features**  Stocky, rotund baleen whale; large head with lumpy projections; broad back, no dorsal fin; body color black to dark brown with irregular white patch on belly; large flippers are narrow at the base; broad tail fluke

**Habits**  Single female is mated by several males; commonly found in groups of 2 or 3, but sometimes in groups of up to 12; larger groups may form at feeding grounds

**Breeding**  Single calf born about every 3 years after gestation period of approximately 11–12 months. Weaned at 4–8 months; sexually mature at about 10 years. May live to 90–100 years

**Voice**  Burping noises and moans

**Diet**  Tiny shrimp (copepods), larval crustaceans, and other small plankton

**Habitat**  Feeds in cold antarctic seas; migrates in winter to warmer coastal waters to breed

**Distribution**  Polar regions in Southern Hemisphere; mainly between 20 and 60˚S

**Status**  Population: may be fewer than 7,000 animals in total; IUCN Vulnerable; CITES I

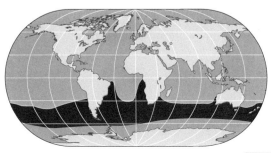

# West Indian Manatee

**Common name** West Indian manatee (Caribbean manatee)

**Scientific name** *Trichechus manatus*

**Family** Trichechidae

**Order** Sirenia

**Size** Length: 12–15 ft (3.7–4.6 m)

**Weight** Up to 1.4 tons (1.2 tonnes)

**Key features** Large, sluggish, and slow-moving creature; grayish-brown in color, with paddle-shaped tail and no hind limbs; skin naked with patches of green algae and a few scattered, bristly hairs; blunt-ended head with thick, fleshy lips and small, piggy eyes

**Habits** Moves slowly, floating and diving in shallow water; often found in small family groups

**Breeding** Single young born after gestation period of about 1 year, with long intervals between births. Weaned at 2 years; sexually mature at 8 years. May live at least 28 years, probably considerably longer

**Voice** Normally silent

**Diet** Aquatic plants, floating and submerged; also grass and other vegetation overhanging from riverbanks

**Habitat** Estuaries, large rivers, and shallow seas

**Distribution** Florida, Caribbean, and coastal waters of South America as far as Brazil

**Status** Population: probably about 10,000–12,000; IUCN Vulnerable; CITES I

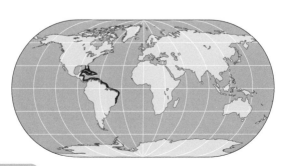

# Dugong

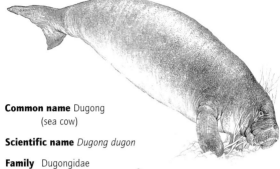

**Common name** Dugong
(sea cow)

**Scientific name** *Dugong dugon*

**Family** Dugongidae

**Order** Sirenia

**Size** Length: 8–9 ft
(2.4–2.7 m),
occasionally up
to 13 ft (4 m)

**Weight** 300–800 lb (136–360 kg), occasionally up to 2,000 lb
(900 kg)

**Key features** Large seal- or whalelike mammal with gray, almost
hairless skin; front flippers bent at an angle part way
along; small eyes and large upper lip with tough, bristly
pads; flat, crescent-shaped tail; no hind limbs

**Habits** Floats lazily in shallow water, diving occasionally
to eat plants from seabed; usually seen singly or
in small groups

**Breeding** Single young born at intervals of 3–7 years (twins rare)
after gestation period of 13–14 months. Young first
graze at 3 months, weaned at 18 months; sexually
mature at 9–10 years. May live over 70 years

**Voice** Generally silent, but occasional chirps and whistles

**Diet** Mostly sea grasses; sometimes green or brown seaweeds

**Habitat** Shallow seas along tropical coasts

**Distribution** Indian Ocean and southwestern Pacific up to 27°
north and south of equator

**Status** Population: probably fewer than 150,000 spread over a
huge area; IUCN Vulnerable; CITES Australian
population II; elsewhere I

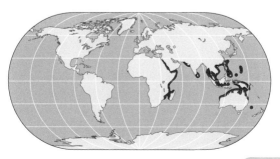

# Demidoff's Bush Baby

**Common name**
Demidoff's bush baby (Demidoff's dwarf galago)

**Scientific name** *Galagoides demidoff*

**Family** Galagonidae

**Order** Primates

**Size** Length head/body: 3–6 in (7–15 cm); tail length: 8–10 in (20–26 cm)

**Weight** 1.5–3.4 oz (43–96 g)

**Key features** Gray-black to reddish coat with paler yellowish underparts; white stripe between eyes and down bridge of nose; pointed, upturned nose and relatively short ears

**Habits** Nocturnal; lively: runs along branches and leaps in tree canopy; sleeps in hollow trees, dense vegetation, or in nests; females may sleep in huddles of 10 or more; forages alone

**Breeding** Usually 1 young, sometimes 2, born per year after gestation period of 110–114 days. Weaned at 2 months; sexually mature at 8–9 months. May live 12 or more years in captivity, probably fewer in the wild

**Voice** Series of loud chirps, increasing to a crescendo; buzzing alarm call

**Diet** Insects: mainly beetles, moths, caterpillars, and crickets; also gum (tree sap) and some fruit

**Habitat** Dense secondary growth; forest edges or land running along the sides of roads

**Distribution** Equatorial western and central Africa

**Status** Population: relatively abundant; CITES II. Numerous in places, although not often seen

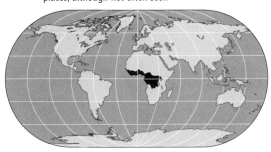

# Slow Loris

**Common name**
Slow loris

**Scientific name**
*Nycticebus coucang*

**Family**  Lorisiidae

**Order**  Primates

**Size**  Length head/body: 10–15 in (25–38 cm); tail length: 2 in (5 cm)

**Weight**  0.8–4.5 lb (0.3–2 kg)

**Key features**  Plump animal with dense, woolly coat; red-gray to gray-brown with paler underside; dark stripe along back and dark circles around large eyes; pale muzzle and small ears; arms and legs same length, tail short

**Habits**  Very slow moving; lives in trees; generally solitary

**Breeding**  One, occasionally 2, young born any time of year after gestation period of 185–197 days. Weaned at 6 months; sexually mature at 18–24 months. May live up to 26 years in captivity, probably fewer in the wild

**Voice**  Whistles, growls, snarls, chirrs, and buzzing noises

**Diet**  Insects (often foul smelling or poisonous); mollusks (such as giant snails); lizards, small birds and mammals, and eggs; some plant food, including gum and fruit; finds most of its food by smell

**Habitat**  Tropical rain forest

**Distribution**  Southeast Asia and western Indonesia

**Status**  Population: unknown, possibly about 1 million; CITES II. Not yet threatened, but declining due to habitat loss

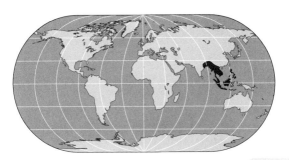

# Ruffed Lemur

**Common name** Ruffed lemur

**Scientific name** *Varecia variegata*

**Family** Lemuridae

**Order** Primates

**Size** Length head/body: 20–22 in (51–56 cm); tail length: 22–26 in (56–66 cm)

**Weight** 7.3–10 lb (3.3–4.5 kg)

**Key features** Large lemur with long, dense fur, especially around neck; 2 subspecies: black-and-white ruffed lemur has patched black-and-white coat; red-ruffed lemur is chestnut-red with black legs, face, and tail; white patch on neck

**Habits** Lives in flexible, mixed-sex groups; spends most of its time in trees; active during the day and the early part of the night, with peaks of activity in the morning and again in the late afternoon and early evening

**Breeding** Two to 4 young born after gestation period of 90–102 days. Weaned at 4–5 months; sexually mature at 2–4 years. May live over 30 years in captivity, slightly fewer in the wild

**Voice** Variety of calls, including loud barks and roars

**Diet** Mainly fruit; also nectar, leaves, seeds, and occasional small birds and rodents

**Habitat** Primary and secondary rain forest

**Distribution** Eastern Madagascar

**Status** Population: fewer than 29,000; IUCN Critically Endangered (subspecies *V. v. ruber*), Endangered (subspecies *V. v. variegata*); CITES II. Declining due to habitat loss; vulnerable to removal of fruit trees

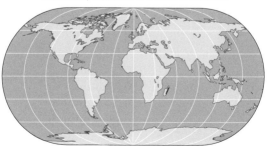

# Aye-Aye

**Common name** Aye-aye

**Scientific name** *Daubentonia madagascariensis*

**Family** Daubentoniidae

**Order** Primates

**Size** Length head/body: 12–15 in (30–38 cm); tail length: 17–22 in (43–56 cm)

**Weight** 4.4–6.6 lb (2–3 kg)

**Key features** Largest nocturnal lemur; long, shaggy coat, dark gray-brown; tail long and bushy; short face with round, pink nose, large ears, and large, orange eyes; hands with long, thin fingers and long, nail-like claws; middle finger elongated and bony

**Habits** Nocturnal; mainly solitary

**Breeding** Single baby born every 2–3 years after gestation period of 170 days. Weaned at 7 months; sexually mature at 2–3 years. May live about 23 years in captivity, over 20 in the wild

**Voice** Variety of calls, including a short "cree"

**Diet** Insect larvae and fruit, including coconuts and mangoes

**Habitat** Rain forest, humid forest, deciduous forest, mangroves, thickets, and plantations

**Distribution** Eastern and northern Madagascar, with small population on western side

**Status** Population: unknown, perhaps a few thousand; IUCN Endangered; CITES I. Like other lemurs, at risk when forest cut down. Feared as bad omen and killed on sight; some shot by farmers; a few killed to eat. Very rare

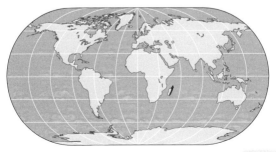

# Ringtailed Lemur

**Common name** Ringtailed lemur

**Scientific name** *Lemur catta*

**Family** Lemuridae

**Order** Primates

**Size** Length head/body: 15–18 in (38–45 cm); tail length: 22–25 in (56–63 cm)

**Weight** 5–7.7 lb (2.3–3.5 kg)

**Key features** Cat-sized animal with dense, pale-gray fur; underparts pale; white face with black eye patches; long black-and-white banded tail, usually held upright

**Habits** Active during the day; feeds in trees but also spends a lot of time on the ground

**Breeding** Single infant (occasionally twins) born between August and November after gestation period of approximately 136 days. Weaned at 4 months; sexually mature at 2 or 3 years. May live over 30 years in captivity, fewer in the wild

**Voice** Catlike mews, grunts, yaps, howls, and purrs

**Diet** Mainly fruit; also leaves, bark, and sap

**Habitat** Dry deciduous scrub and forest

**Distribution** South and southwestern Madagascar

**Status** Population: fewer than 100,000; IUCN Endangered; CITES II. Declining due to loss of habitat

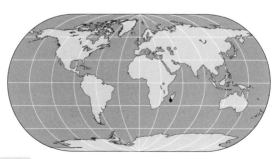

# Common Marmoset

**Common name** Common marmoset

**Scientific name** *Callithrix jacchus*

**Family** Callitrichidae

**Order** Primates

**Size** Length head/body: 4.7–6 in (12–15 cm); tail length: 12–14 in (30–35 cm)

**Weight** 10.5–12.7 oz (300–360 g)

**Key features** Mottled gray-brown coat; crown blackish with white patch on forehead; long white ear tufts; gray-and-white banded tail

**Habits** Diurnal; lives in stable groups of up to 15 animals

**Breeding** One to 4 young (often twins) born twice yearly after gestation period of 130–150 days. Weaned at 100 days; males sexually mature at 11–15 months, females at 14–24 months. May live 16 years in captivity, 10 in the wild

**Voice** Soft "phee" contact call; angry chatter and high-pitched whistle as a warning call

**Diet** Tree sap, insects, spiders, fruit, flowers, and nectar; also lizards, frogs, eggs, and nestlings

**Habitat** Atlantic coast forest and gallery forest along rivers; forest patches in dry thorn scrub and bush savanna

**Distribution** Northeastern Brazil west and south from the Rio Parnaiba

**Status** Population: abundant; CITES I. Relatively common and widespread; not seriously threatened

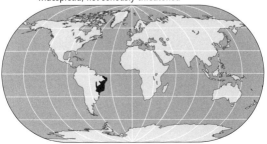

# Golden Lion Tamarin

**Common name** Golden lion tamarin

**Scientific name** *Leontopithecus rosalia*

**Family** Callitrichidae

**Order** Primates

**Size** Length head/body: 8–13 in (20–31 cm); tail length: 12.5–16 in (32–40 cm)

**Weight** 21–28 oz (600–800 g)

**Key features** Small, lively monkey; long, silky golden coat; long hair on crown, cheeks, and sides of neck forms mane; long tail; bare, flattened face with widely spaced nostrils

**Habits** Social; lives in small groups of 3–7 individuals; active during the day, spending most of the time in the dense middle layers of the forest; rests at night in tree holes

**Breeding** Young (most commonly twins) born September–March after gestation period of 128 days. Weaned at 12 weeks; sexually mature at 2–3 years. May live 28 years in captivity, many fewer in the wild

**Voice** A variety of calls, including trills, clucks, and whines

**Diet** Mostly fruit and insects; small animals such as frogs and lizards; also birds' eggs

**Habitat** Lowland tropical forests from sea level to about 3,000 ft (1,000 m)

**Distribution** Rio de Janeiro state, southeastern Brazil

**Status** Population: fewer than 1,000; IUCN Critically Endangered; CITES I. Destruction of lowland forest is greatest threat to survival

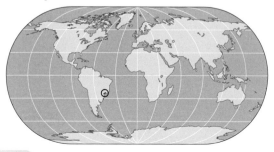

# Northern Night Monkey

**Common name** Northern night monkey (owl monkey, douroucouli)

**Scientific name** *Aotus trivirgatus*

**Family** Cebidae

**Order** Primates

**Size** Length head/body: 12–16.5 in (30–42 cm); tail length: 10–17 in (25–43 cm)

**Weight** 1.8–2.8 lb (0.8–1.3 kg)

**Key features** Grizzled brown or gray on back, limbs, and back of head; underside buff-white; head has triangular white patches above large eyes; 3 black stripes run between and either side of eyes, converging on top of head

**Habits** Nocturnal; arboreal; lives in family groups of 2–5

**Breeding** Usually a single offspring born any time of year after gestation period of 120–133 days. Weaned at 6–8 months; sexually mature at 3 years. May live about 27 years in captivity, 10–15 in the wild

**Voice** Wide variety of calls, including shrill cries, hoots, grunts, clicks, and squeaks

**Diet** Small fruit; also leaves, nectar, plant gums, insects, eggs, and small animals, such as lizards and frogs

**Habitat** Forests from sea level to 10,500 ft (3,200 m)

**Distribution** Tropical Central and South America: Panama, Brazil, Venezuela, and Peru

**Status** Population: probably low thousands; CITES II. Widespread and fairly abundant

# Humboldt's Woolly Monkey

**Common name** Humboldt's woolly monkey (common woolly monkey)

**Scientific name** *Lagothrix lagotricha*

**Family** Cebidae

**Order** Primates

**Size** Length head/body: 18–25.5 in (46–65 cm); tail length: 21–30.5 in (53–77 cm)

**Weight** Male 8–22 lb (3.6–10 kg); female 7.5–14.5 lb (3.4–6.5 kg)

**Key features** Fur dense and moderately long; body gray to olive-brown or dark brown; the rounded head is often darker, almost black; strong prehensile tail

**Habits** Diurnal; prefers to stay high up in tree canopy; lives in mixed-sex groups of 20–70

**Breeding** Single baby born every 1.5–3 years after gestation period of 223 days. Weaned at 9–12 months; sexually mature at 6–8 years. May live 24 years in captivity, 10 in the wild

**Voice** Range of yelps, screams, chuckles, and barks

**Diet** Fruit; also leaves and other vegetable material

**Habitat** Mature, undisturbed rain forest from sea level to 9,850 ft (3,000 m)

**Distribution** Bolivia, Brazil, Colombia, Ecuador, Peru, and Venezuela

**Status** Population: probably many thousands; IUCN Critically Endangered (1 subspecies); Vulnerable (2 subspecies); CITES II. Relatively abundant, not considered to be at risk

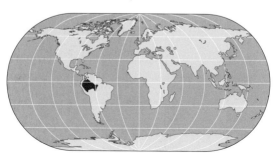

# Red Uakari

**Common name**
Red uakari (bald uakari, white uakari)

**Scientific name** *Cacajao calvus*

**Family** Cebidae

**Order** Primates

**Size** Length head/body: 21–22 in
(54–57 cm); tail length: 5.5–7.3 in (14–18.5 cm)

**Weight** Male 7.6 lb (3.4 kg); female 6.4 lb (2.9 kg)

**Key features** Small monkey with long, coarse, pale-brown fur
and bare, red face; tail very short

**Habits** Tree dwelling, but often descends to the ground; lives in
social groups numbering 15–30 animals; active by day

**Breeding** One young born every 2 years or so after gestation
period of about 6 months. Weaned at 20 months;
females sexually mature at 3 years, males at 5 years.
May live over 30 years in captivity, 10 in the wild

**Voice** Generally silent, except during noisy fights

**Diet** Mostly seeds, but also flowers, fruit, leaves, and insects

**Habitat** Wet lowland forests

**Distribution** South America: Upper Amazon into eastern Peru
and southern Colombia

**Status** Population: unknown, probably many thousands;
IUCN Endangered (3 local subspecies); Vulnerable
(1 subspecies); CITES I. Fairly common, but threatened
by hunting and forest clearance; certain subspecies rare

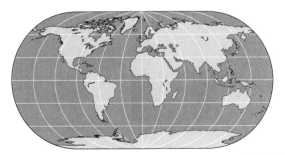

# Squirrel Monkey

**Common name** Squirrel monkey (common squirrel monkey)

**Scientific name** *Saimiri sciureus*

**Family** Cebidae

**Order** Primates

**Size** Length head/body: 11-14.5 in (28-37 cm); tail length: 14.5-18 in (37-45 cm)

**Weight** 19-44 oz (550-1,250 g)

**Key features** Small olive-green monkey with orange hands and white around the face; muzzle black

**Habits** Active by day in groups of 30-40 animals

**Breeding** Single young born once a year after gestation period of 170 days. Weaned at about 1 year; females sexually mature at 3 years, males at 5 years. May live up to 30 years in captivity, probably fewer in the wild

**Voice** Variety of squeaks, chirps, and purring noises

**Diet** Mainly fruit and insects

**Habitat** Forests, including mangroves from sea level to 6,500 ft (2,000 m)

**Distribution** Tropical South America

**Status** Population: abundant; CITES II. Common animal. Large numbers previously captured for the pet trade, now protected in the wild and no longer threatened by such activities

# Black-Handed Spider Monkey

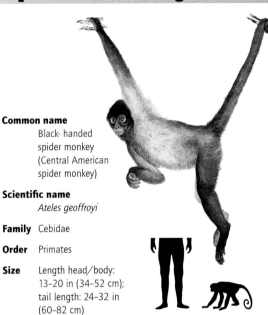

**Common name**
Black-handed spider monkey (Central American spider monkey)

**Scientific name**
*Ateles geoffroyi*

**Family** Cebidae

**Order** Primates

**Size** Length head/body: 13–20 in (34–52 cm); tail length: 24–32 in (60–82 cm)

**Weight** Male 16–20 lb (7–9 kg); female 13–20 lb (6–9 kg)

**Key features** Short, thin fur of various shades of brown, with black hands and feet; long, slender limbs and long tail; face often has a mask of pale skin around the eyes and mouth

**Habits** Lives in small groups; swings through trees using hands, feet, and tail; active by day

**Breeding** Single young born every 2 or 3 years at any time of year after gestation period of 225 days. Weaned at 1 year; sexually mature at about 5 years. May live up to 48 years in captivity, more than 20 in the wild

**Voice** Barks and screams

**Diet** Mainly fruit and leaves; also tree bark

**Habitat** High tree canopy; rarely on the ground

**Distribution** Central America from Mexico to Panama

**Status** Population: fairly abundant, probably many thousands; IUCN Endangered (4 local subspecies), Vulnerable (3 local subspecies); CITES I. Still fairly common in some places

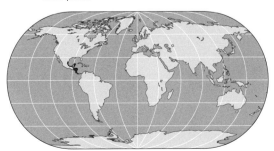

# Brown Howler Monkey

**Common name** Brown howler monkey

**Scientific name** *Alouatta fusca*

**Family** Cebidae

**Order** Primates

**Size** Length head/body: 18-23 in (45-58 cm); tail length: 20-26 in (50-66 cm). Male generally larger than female

**Weight** 9-16 lb (4-7 kg)

**Key features** Thickset monkey, with swollen throat region in adult males; coat dark reddish brown, paler below

**Habits** Tree dwelling; lives in small groups; active mainly during daylight hours

**Breeding** Single young born each year after gestation period of about 189 days. Weaned at about 10-12 months; females sexually mature at 3-4 years, males take longer. May live to about 20 years in captivity, 15 in the wild

**Voice** Very loud howling and roars made especially by males

**Diet** Mainly leaves, but also fruit

**Habitat** Tropical forests

**Distribution** Coastal forests of southeastern Brazil

**Status** Population: unknown, probably low thousands; IUCN Vulnerable; CITES II. Threatened by destruction and fragmentation of forest habitat

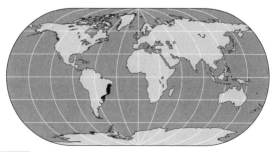

# Proboscis Monkey

**Common name** Proboscis monkey

**Scientific name** *Nasalis larvatus*

**Family** Cercopithecidae

**Order** Primates

**Size** Length head/body: male 24–30 in (60–76 cm); female 21–24 in (53–60 cm); tail length: 22–24 in (56–60 cm)

**Weight** Male 35–55 lb (16–25 kg); female 15–24 lb (7–11 kg)

**Key features** Long, dangling nose in adult males, less developed in females

**Habits** Mainly active in late afternoon to dark; lives in small social groups

**Breeding** Single young born at any time of year after gestation period of 106 days. Weaned at 7 months; sexually mature at about 3 years. May live up to 23 years in captivity, usually fewer in the wild

**Voice** Males make a long, drawn-out resonant honk; female call is a milder sound, similar to that of a goose

**Diet** Mainly leaves, but fruit and flowers also eaten when available

**Habitat** Found near fresh water in lowland rain forests or mangrove swamps

**Distribution** Borneo and Mentawai Islands in the Malay Archipelago

**Status** Population: probably fewer than 250,000; IUCN Vulnerable; CITES I. Habitat destruction is threatening populations; hunting is also on the increase

# Black-and-White Colobus Monkey

**Common name** Black-and-white colobus monkey (white-epauleted black colobus monkey, Angola colobus monkey)

**Scientific name** *Colobus angolensis*

**Family** Cercopithecidae

**Order** Primates

**Size** Length head/body: 20–26 in (50–66 cm); tail length: 25–35 in (63–89 cm)

**Weight** 20–44 lb (9–20 kg)

**Key features** Large black monkey with white cheeks and long, flowing white cape around shoulders

**Habits** Spends almost all its time up in trees; active during the day; lives in small family groups

**Breeding** One young born every 20 months or so after gestation period of 6 months. Weaned at about 6 months; females sexually mature at about 4 years, males at 6 years. May live 30 years in captivity, fewer in the wild

**Voice** Loud croaking and roaring chorus at dawn and dusk, otherwise usually silent; sometimes makes a loud cough

**Diet** Mostly leaves; some fruit and seeds

**Habitat** Mountain and lowland forests

**Distribution** Central African forests; scattered localities in Tanzania

**Status** Fairly common; IUCN Vulnerable (some small, isolated populations); CITES II. Apart from habitat loss, the main threat to colobus monkeys is hunting for their skins, which have been popular with tourists

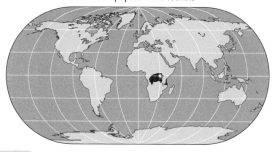

# Hanuman Langur

**Common name**
Hanuman langur

**Scientific name**
*Semnopithecus entellus*

**Family** Cercopithecidae

**Order** Primates

**Size** Length head/body: 16–31 in (41–78 cm); tail length: 27–42.5 in (69–108 cm)

**Weight** Male 20–66 lb (9–30 kg); female 16.5–40 lb (7.5–18 kg)

**Key features** Slender, agile monkey; long tail; upperparts gray, brown, or buff; crown and underparts white or yellowish; black face, ears, hands, and feet; prominent brow ridge

**Habits** Active by day in small social groups dominated by 1 or more males; forages on ground as well as in trees

**Breeding** Usually a single offspring born after gestation period of 190–210 days. Weaned at 10–12 months; females sexually mature at 3–4 years, males at 6–7 years. May live about 25 years in captivity, 15 in the wild

**Voice** Resonant whoops and guttural alarm calls

**Diet** Mainly leaves; also some fruits, seeds, flowers, and sometimes crops

**Habitat** Varied: includes wet tropical forests, shrubs, desert edges, alpine scrub, and urban areas

**Distribution** From Pakistan through Himalayas to Nepal and Bangladesh; India and Sri Lanka

**Status** Population: probably about half a million; Indian population estimated at 233,800 (1986); IUCN Lower Risk: near threatened; CITES I

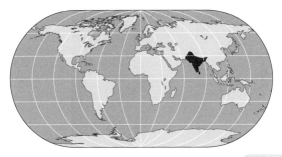

# Mandrill

**Common name** Mandrill

**Scientific name** *Mandrillus sphinx*

**Family** Cercopithecidae

**Order** Primates

**Size** Length head/body: 22–37 in (55–95 cm); tail length: 2–3 in (5–8 cm)

**Weight** Male 42–66 lb (19–30 kg); female 22–33 lb (10–15 kg)

**Key features** Olive-brown, heavily built baboon; male has a brightly colored face and posterior

**Habits** Lives in small, male-dominated groups; active during the day, mostly on the ground; retires to trees at night to sleep

**Breeding** Single young born at intervals of 1–2 years after gestation period of 175 days. Weaned at 1 year; sexually mature at 4–5 years. May live more than 45 years in captivity, probably many fewer in the wild

**Voice** Individuals often silent; larger groups are noisy, making chorus of double barks; sometimes grunts and squeals

**Diet** Prefers fruits, but will eat almost anything, including small animals

**Habitat** Mainly evergreen coastal forest

**Distribution** Equatorial West Africa

**Status** Population: unknown, but declining; IUCN Vulnerable; CITES I

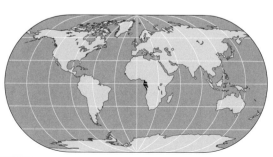

# Hamadryas Baboon

**Common name** Hamadryas baboon (sacred baboon)

**Scientific name** *Papio hamadryas*

**Family** Cercopithecidae

**Order** Primates

**Size** Length head/body: male 27.5–37 in (70–95 cm); female 20–25.5 in (50–65 cm); tail length: 16.5–24 in (42–60 cm)

**Weight** Male 37–55.5 lb (17–25 kg); female 22–29.5 lb (10–13 kg)

**Key features** Dull-brown to silver-gray coat with longer hair over shoulders, especially in adult males; red patch of skin over hips and naked red face with prominent side ridges on long muzzle

**Habits** Walks on all fours; lives in bands of males, each with a harem of females; bands come together to sleep

**Breeding** Usually a single baby born after gestation period of 5–6 months. Weaned at around 1 year; females sexually mature at 3.5 years, males at 2 years. May live up to about 40 years in captivity, 30–40 in the wild

**Voice** Variety of barks and grunts

**Diet** Grass, fruit, seeds, bulbs, insects, hares, and young ungulates; sometimes raids crops

**Habitat** Arid subdesert, steppe, and bare highlands

**Distribution** Northeastern Sudan, eastern Ethiopia, and northern Somalia; also east of Red Sea in Yemen and Saudi Arabia

**Status** Population: likely to be in the thousands; IUCN Lower Risk: near threatened; CITES II. A vulnerable species

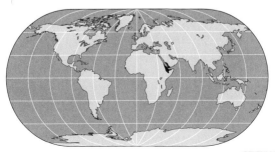

# Savanna Baboon

**Common name** Savanna baboon (yellow baboon)

**Scientific name** *Papio cynocephalus*

**Family** Cercopithecidae

**Order** Primates

**Size** Length head/body: male 31–45 in (79–114 cm); female 20–28 in (51–71 cm); tail length: 18–27 in (46–68 cm)

**Weight** Male 48–66 lb (22–30 kg); female 24–33 lb (11–15 kg)

**Key features** Coat yellowish-gray; shiny black patch of bare skin over buttocks; eyes set close together with prominent brow-ridge above; long, ridged muzzle; powerful jaws with long canine teeth in adult males

**Habits** Active during the day; forages on the ground and in trees; lives in large troops averaging 30–40 members

**Breeding** Usually single baby born every 1–2 years after gestation period of 6 months. Weaned at 1 year; females sexually mature at 5 years, males at 7 years. May live up to 40 years in captivity, 20–30 in the wild

**Voice** Barks, grunts, screeches, yelps, and clicks

**Diet** Grass, fruit, seeds, bulbs, lichen, mushrooms, insects, young ungulates, and crops

**Habitat** Savanna grassland, open woodland and forest edge, rocky hill country, and semidesert with some grass and thorn bush

**Distribution** Widespread in central and eastern Africa

**Status** Population: unknown—tens of thousands; IUCN Lower Risk: near threatened; CITES II. Fairly common primate

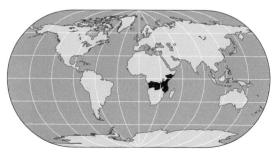

# Barbary Macaque

**Common name** Barbary macaque (Barbary ape)

**Scientific name** *Macaca sylvanus*

**Family** Cercopithecidae

**Order** Primates

**Size** Length head/body: 22–30 in (55–76 cm). Female about 20% smaller than male

**Weight** 10–20 lb (4.5–9 kg)

**Key features** Grayish-brown monkey with almost no tail; face hairless with large cheek pouches to store food

**Habits** Lives in small groups of up to about 40 animals (usually fewer); spends more time on the ground than other macaques; active during the day

**Breeding** Single young born at any time of year after gestation period of 210 days. Weaned at about 1 year; females sexually mature at 2–4 years, males at 5–7 years. May live up to about 30 years in captivity, about 20 in the wild

**Voice** Wide range of typical monkey sounds

**Diet** Mostly plant material, including fruit and leaves, seeds, shoots, acorns, tubers, bark, and pine needles; some animal food such as insects (especially caterpillars)

**Habitat** Rocky mountain slopes and montane woodland

**Distribution** Morocco, Algeria, Tunisia, and Gibraltar

**Status** Population: about 15,000; IUCN Vulnerable; CITES II. Once found widely across North Africa, but now reduced to a few scattered populations

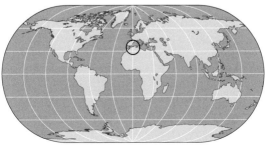

# Japanese Macaque

**Common name** Japanese macaque (snow monkey)

**Scientific name** *Macaca fuscata*

**Family** Cercopithecidae

**Order** Primates

**Size** Length head/body: 18.5-24 in (47-60 cm); tail length: 3-5 in (7-12 cm)

**Weight** Male 22-40 lb (10-18 kg); female 15.5-26.5 lb (7-12 kg)

**Key features** Thick, brown to gray coat; bare, red-colored face and buttocks; short tail

**Habits** Active by day; highly social: lives in troops averaging 20-30 animals, but sometimes up to 100; forages on ground and in trees

**Breeding** Single infant born every 2 years (usually between May and September) after gestation period of 5-6 months. Weaned at 6 months; females sexually mature at 3-4 years, but usually first breed at 6, males sexually mature at 5-6 years. May live up to about 30 years in captivity, similar in the wild

**Voice** Various long- and short-distance calls

**Diet** Fruit, insects, young leaves, and small animals; sometimes raids crops

**Habitat** Upland and mountain broad-leaved forest

**Distribution** Japan

**Status** Population: about 35,000-50,000 (1990); IUCN previously Endangered, temporarily listed as Data Deficient (2000); CITES II. Listed as Threatened by U.S. Endangered Species Act, but status in wild disputed

# Vervet Monkey

**Common name** Vervet monkey (savanna guenon, grivet, or green monkey)

**Scientific name** *Cercopithecus aethiops*

**Family** Cercopithecidae

**Order** Primates

**Size** Length head/body: male 20–26 in (50–65 cm); female 15–24 in (38–62 cm); tail length: 19–30 in (48–75 cm)

**Weight** Male 9–18 lb (4–8 kg); female 8–11 lb (4–5 kg)

**Key features** Back and outer limbs grizzled gray or olive, underparts white; dark hands, feet, and tip of tail; face is bare and black, with white cheek tufts and eyebrows; eyelids white; scrotum bright blue, penis red

**Habits** Alert, lively, sociable monkey; active during the day; spends time on the ground as well as in trees

**Breeding** Single young usually born in favorable season after gestation period of 7 months. Weaned at 8–9 months; females sexually mature at 2 years, males at 3 years. May live up to about 30 years in captivity, 10 in the wild

**Voice** Includes barks, grunts, and screams

**Diet** Mainly fruit; also leaves, flowers, and crops; occasionally insects, eggs, nestlings, and small animals

**Habitat** Savanna and woodland edges near water

**Distribution** Most of Africa: Senegal east to Somalia and south to South Africa

**Status** Population: abundant, many thousands. Common and widespread

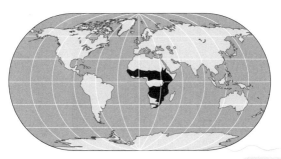

# Lar Gibbon

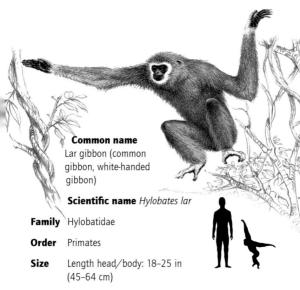

**Common name**
Lar gibbon (common gibbon, white-handed gibbon)

**Scientific name** *Hylobates lar*

**Family** Hylobatidae

**Order** Primates

**Size** Length head/body: 18–25 in (45–64 cm)

**Weight** 12–14 lb (5–6 kg)

**Key features** Coat color varies between populations—either black, dark brown, reddish brown, or light buff; long, spindly limbs with pale hands and feet; no tail; pale ring around face

**Habits** Lives high in rain-forest trees, swinging between branches; active by day; family groups are territorial, announcing their presence with loud calls

**Breeding** Single infant born about every 2 years after gestation period of 7–8 months. Weaned at 20 months; sexually mature at 6–7 years. May live up to about 40 years in captivity, 30–40 in the wild

**Voice** Male's song is simple hoots, female's longer, rising to a climax

**Diet** Mainly fruit; also leaves, birds, and insects

**Habitat** Evergreen rain forest; semideciduous monsoon forest

**Distribution** Thailand, Malay Peninsula, and northern Sumatra

**Status** Population: about 79,000 (1987); IUCN Endangered; CITES I

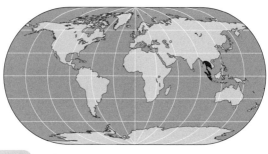

# Bonobo

**Common name**
Bonobo (pygmy chimpanzee)

**Scientific name**
*Pan paniscus*

**Family** Hominidae

**Order** Primates

**Size** Length head/body: 27.5–33 in (70–83 cm)

**Weight** Male up to 88 lb (40 kg); female up to 68 lb (31 kg)

**Key features** Looks like a long-legged chimpanzee, but body more slender with narrower shoulders; skin of face dark brown to black

**Habits** Active during the day in trees and on the ground; sleeps in nests built among tree branches; social groups more female centered, with the most dominant female ranking above the dominant male

**Breeding** Single young born at any time of year after gestation period of 220–230 days. Weaned at 4 years; females sexually mature at 9 years, males earlier, although both unlikely to breed until older. May live to possibly 30 years in the wild, rarely kept in captivity

**Voice** Calls more high pitched than chimpanzee

**Diet** Fruit, leaves, stems, shoots, and honey; also termites, ants, and small reptiles

**Habitat** Tropical lowland rain forest

**Distribution** Restricted to northern-central Democratic Republic of Congo south of Congo River and between the Kasai and Sankuru Rivers

**Status** Population: about 15,000; IUCN Endangered; CITES I. Habitat loss and hunting have contributed to decline

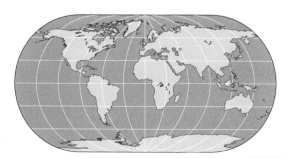

# Chimpanzee

**Common name** Chimpanzee

**Scientific name** *Pan troglodytes*

**Family** Hominidae

**Order** Primates

**Size** Length head/body: male 27.5-35 in (70-89 cm); female 25-33 in (63-84 cm); height: 39-66 in (99-168 cm)

**Weight** Male 75-154 lb (34-70 kg); female 57-110 lb (26-50 kg)

**Key features** Coat brownish or black, graying with age; face bare and brownish pink

**Habits** Diurnal; nights spent in platform nests in trees; usually travels on ground and seen in groups; sometimes walks upright, but usually on all fours using knuckles of hands

**Breeding** Single young born every 5 or 6 years after gestation period of about 230 days. Weaned at 3.5-4.5 years; sexually mature at around 7 years, but females do not breed until aged 14-15, males at 15-16 years. May live up to 60 years in captivity, similar in the wild

**Voice** Wide range of calls, including hoots, barks, grunts, and screams

**Diet** Varied; includes fruit, flowers, seeds, bark, insects, birds' eggs, and meat

**Habitat** Deciduous, montane, and tropical rain forests; also patchy savanna woodland

**Distribution** Western and central Africa

**Status** Population: 150-230,000; IUCN Vulnerable; CITES I. Threatened due to deforestation

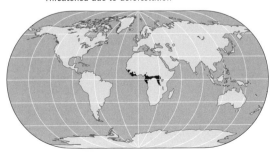

# Western Lowland Gorilla

**Common name** Western lowland gorilla

**Scientific name** *Gorilla gorilla gorilla*

**Family** Hominidae

**Order** Primates

**Size** Height: male about 5.5 ft (1.7 m), occasionally to 5.9 ft (1.8 m); female 5 ft (1.5 m); arm span: 7.5 ft (2.3 m)

**Weight** Male 310–450 lb (140–204 kg); female 200 lb (90 kg)

**Key features** Largest primate; bulky body; arms longer than legs; coat relatively short and brown to dark gray; mature males have silver-gray back; broad face with fairly small jaws

**Habits** Lives in small groups of 4 to 8 animals, with 1 dominant "silverback" male; active during the day, nights spent in nests; docile, spends around a third of the day resting

**Breeding** Usually 1 young born every 4 years after gestation period of 250–270 days. Weaned at 2.5–3 years; females sexually mature at 6–8 years, males at 8–10 years. May live 50 years in captivity, 35 in the wild

**Voice** Roars, growls, barks, grunts, purrs, croaks, hoots, squeaks, and screeches

**Diet** Fruit, seeds, leaves, plant stems, bark, and invertebrates such as termites and caterpillars

**Habitat** Swamp and tropical forest

**Distribution** Central-western Africa

**Status** Population: fewer than 50,000; IUCN Endangered; CITES I. Vulnerable to poaching and habitat loss

# Mountain Gorilla

**Common name** Mountain gorilla (eastern gorilla)

**Scientific name** *Gorilla beringei beringei*

**Family** Hominidae

**Order** Primates

**Size** Height (upright): male 4.6–5.9 ft (1.4–1.8 m); female 4.3–5 ft (1.3–1.5 m); arm span: 7.5 ft (2.3 m)

**Weight** Male up to 400 lb (181 kg); female up to 200 lb (90 kg)

**Key features** Large, bulky ape with barrel-shaped body; arms muscular, longer than legs; coat blue-black, turning gray with age, males with silver patch on back; hair short on back, long elsewhere; broad face and massive jaws

**Habits** Social groups of 5–30 animals centered around 1 dominant "silverback" male; docile, mostly feeds or rests; males display strength by chest-beating

**Breeding** Usually 1 baby born every 4 years after 250–270 days' gestation. Weaned at 2.5–3 years; female sexually mature at 8–10 years, male at 10. May live 35 years

**Voice** Howling, roaring, grunting, and snarling

**Diet** Leaves, stems, berries, roots, pulp, and bark

**Habitat** Montane rain forest and subalpine scrub at altitudes of 5,400–12,400 ft (1,645–3,780 m)

**Distribution** Borders of Democratic Republic of Congo, Rwanda, and Uganda

**Status** Population: about 320; IUCN Critically Endangered; CITES I. Most threatened gorilla species

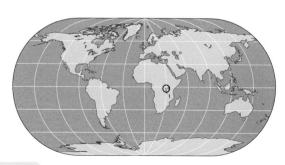

# Orangutans

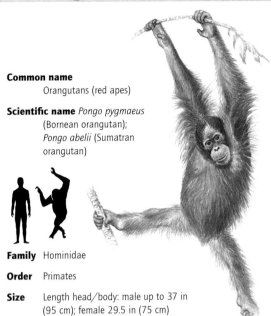

**Common name**
Orangutans (red apes)

**Scientific name** *Pongo pygmaeus*
(Bornean orangutan);
*Pongo abelii* (Sumatran
orangutan)

**Family** Hominidae

**Order** Primates

**Size** Length head/body: male up to 37 in
(95 cm); female 29.5 in (75 cm)

**Weight** Male 130–200 lb (59–91 kg); female 88–110 lb
(40–50 kg)

**Key features** Very long arms; feet are handlike; coat
sparse and coarse, ranging from orange to dark brown

**Habits** Solitary; spends most of its time in treetops; active
during the day, rests overnight in nests among branches

**Breeding** Single young born about every 8 years after gestation
period of 8 months. Weaned at about 3 years; females
sexually mature at 12 years, males at 15 years. May live
60 years in captivity, 45–50 in the wild

**Voice** Males make loud resonant calls with the help of their
large throat pouches at a volume comparable to that of
a lion's roar

**Diet** Fruit (such as mangoes and figs), young shoots, bark,
and insects

**Habitat** Lowland and hilly tropical rain forest

**Distribution** Confined to the islands of Sumatra (Indonesia) and
lowland Borneo

**Status** Population: about 20,000; IUCN Endangered; CITES I.
Forest clearance is biggest threat

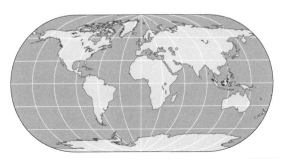

# African Elephant

**Common name** African elephant

**Scientific name** *Loxodonta africana*

**Family** Elephantidae

**Order** Proboscidea

**Size** Length head/body (including trunk): 20–25 ft (6–7.5 m); tail length: 40–60 in (100–150 cm); height at shoulder: male 10.8 ft (3.3 m); female 8.9 ft (2.7 m).

**Weight** Male up to 6.8 tons (6 tonnes); female up to 3.4 tons (3 tonnes)

**Key features** Gray body; large head and ears; long ivory tusks; flexible trunk; skin with sparsely scattered black, bristly hairs; flat forehead and back; 4 toes on front feet, 3 on hind feet

**Habits** Females live in family groups of typically 2 or 3 sisters, plus offspring

**Breeding** Usually 1 calf born every 3–4 years in wet season after gestation period of 656 days. Weaned at 6 years; female sexually mature at 10 years, male at 25–30 years. May live more than 70 years in captivity, 60 in the wild

**Voice** "Trumpeting," rumbles or "purring," roars, snorts, squeals, screams, and low growls

**Diet** Grasses, tree leaves and fruit, bark

**Habitat** Mainly savanna grassland

**Distribution** Eastern and central Africa south of the Sahara

**Status** Population: fewer than 600,000; IUCN Endangered; CITES I in most countries, II in Botswana, Namibia, and Zimbabwe. Declining species

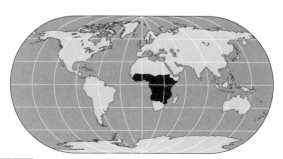

# Asian Elephant

**Common name** Asian elephant

**Scientific name** *Elephas maximus*

**Family** Elephantidae

**Order** Proboscidea

**Size** Length head/body (including trunk): 18–21 ft (5.5–6.4 m); tail length: 4–5 ft (1.2–1.5 m); height at shoulder: 8–10 ft (2.4–3 m)

**Weight** Male up to 6.1 tons (5.4 tonnes); female up to 3 tons (2.7 tonnes)

**Key features** Dark-gray to brown skin; ears smaller than African species; domed forehead and rounded back; only 1 "lip" on upper side of trunk; tusks only appear in some males; 5 toes on front feet, 4 on hind feet

**Habits** Lives in family groups of typically 2–10 related females plus offspring

**Breeding** Usually 1 calf born every 3–4 years in the wet season after gestation period of 615–668 days. Weaned at 6 years; females sexually mature at 15–20 years, males at 20. May live 75–80 years in captivity, 70 in the wild

**Voice** "Trumpeting," rumbles or "purring," roars, snorts, squeals, screams, and low growls

**Diet** Up to 100 wild plant species, plus local crops

**Habitat** Evergreen and dry deciduous forest; thorn scrub, jungle, swamp, and grassland

**Distribution** Indian subcontinent, Sri Lanka, Indochina, parts of Malay Peninsula, Thailand, and Southeast Asian islands

**Status** Population: 37,000–57,000; IUCN Endangered; CITES I. Declining species

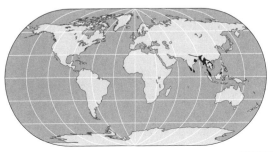

# Rock Hyrax

**Common name** Rock hyrax
(rock dassie, Cape rock hyrax)

**Scientific name** *Procavia capensis*

**Family** Procaviidae

**Order** Hyracoidea

**Size** Length head/body: 12–23 in (30–58 cm)

**Weight** 6.6–8.8 lb (3–4 kg)

**Key features** Rotund body with short legs and no tail; small head with pointed snout, long whiskers, and round ears; fur dense, but coarse and a variable shade of brownish-gray, fading to creamy white on underside

**Habits** Diurnal; basks in sun; social; nimble and fast moving; can be aggressive

**Breeding** Single litter of 1–6 young born in wet season (summer and fall, different in Northern and Southern Hemispheres) after gestation period of 7–8 months. Weaned at 1 month but may suckle for up to 5, sexually mature at 16–17 months. May live up to 11 years in captivity, 8 in the wild

**Voice** Various squeals, whistles, and chattering sounds

**Diet** Wide variety of plant material

**Habitat** Rough scrub and hillsides with plenty of rocky outcrops and crevices

**Distribution** Africa and the Middle East south of a line from Senegal in West Africa to Turkey

**Status** Population: abundant

# White Rhinoceros

**Common name** White rhinoceros (square-lipped rhinoceros, grass rhinoceros)

**Scientific name** *Ceratotherium simum*

**Family** Rhinocerotidae

**Order** Perissodactyla

**Size** Length head/body: 11–14 ft (3.3–4.2 m); tail length: 20–27.5 in (50–70 cm); height at shoulder: 5–6 ft (1.5–1.8 m). Male 20–90% bigger than female

**Weight** 1.9–2.6 tons (1.7–2.3 tonnes)

**Key features** Huge gray-brown rhino with large head, 2 horns, and very square upper lip

**Habits** Active by day and night; dominant males solitary and territorial; wallows in mud or water; generally shy and docile

**Breeding** Single calf born after gestation period of 16 months. Weaned at 12–14 months; sexually mature at 5 years, but males not dominant enough to breed until 10–12 years. May live up to 50 years in captivity, similar in the wild

**Voice** Varied repertoire of grunts, snorts, chirps, squeals, growls, bellows, and pants

**Diet** Grass

**Habitat** Flat, lightly forested plains close to water

**Distribution** Reserves and national parks in southern Africa and Democratic Republic of Congo

**Status** Population: 7,500; IUCN Lower Risk: conservation dependent, Critically Endangered (northern subspecies); CITES I

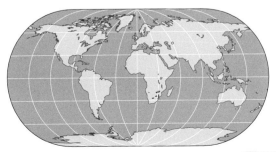

**121**

# Black Rhinoceros

**Common name** Black rhinoceros

**Scientific name** *Diceros bicornis*

**Family** Rhinocerotidae

**Order** Perissodactyla

**Size** Length head/body: 10–12 ft (3–3.7 m); tail length: to 27.5 in (70 cm); height at shoulder: 4.6–6 ft (1.4–1.8 m)

**Weight** 1.2–1.4 tons (0.9–1.3 tonnes). Male and female similar size, but male generally heavier

**Key features** Thick-skinned, dark-gray rhino with 2 horns and protruding, pointed upper lip

**Habits** Usually nonterritorial; most active morning and evening; may also feed at night; rests during the day; wallows in mud; rather unpredictable, very nervous around humans

**Breeding** Single calf born every 2–5 years at any time of year (births peak in rainy season) after gestation period of 15–16 months. Weaned at 2–12 months; females sexually mature at 4–5 years, males at 7–9 years. May live up to 45 years in the wild, similar in captivity

**Voice** Variety of grunts, groans, squeals, snorts, and puffs

**Diet** Browses twigs, leaves, shoots, and bark

**Habitat** Transition zones between forest and grassland; thickets and scrub

**Distribution** Scattered populations in protected areas of sub-Saharan Africa, mostly in the east

**Status** Population: fewer than 3,000; IUCN Critically Endangered; CITES I

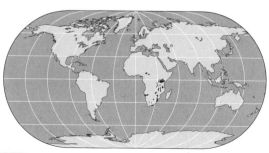

# Indian Rhinoceros

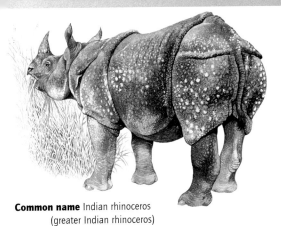

**Common name** Indian rhinoceros (greater Indian rhinoceros)

**Scientific name** *Rhinoceros unicornis*

**Family** Rhinocerotidae

**Order** Perissodactyla

**Size** Length head/body: 10–12.5 ft (3–3.8 m); tail length: up to 28 in (70 cm); height at shoulder: 5–6 ft (1.5–1.8 m)

**Weight** 1.8–2.5 tons (1.6–2.2 tonnes). Male heavier than female

**Key features** Large rhino with single horn; deep skin folds give armor-plated appearance; hide covered in horny bumps; upper lip prehensile

**Habits** Mostly solitary; active at night and around dusk and dawn; wallows in mud and water

**Breeding** Single calf born every 3–5 years at any time of year after gestation period of 16–17 months. Weaned at 12–18 months; sexually mature at 7 years. May live up to 47 years in captivity, probably fewer in the wild

**Voice** Snorts, grunts, bleats, growls, and roars

**Diet** Browses leaves; also eats grass, fruit, twigs, and shoots

**Habitat** Tall grassland, swamp, and forest; increasingly uses cultivated land

**Distribution** Protected areas of northeastern India, Bhutan, and Nepal

**Status** Population: 2,000 in the wild, about 150 in captivity; IUCN Endangered; CITES I. Gradually increasing thanks to protection in reserves; poaching still a serious problem

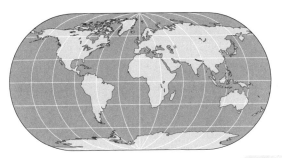

# Plains Zebra

**Common name** Plains zebra (common zebra, Burchell's zebra)

**Scientific name** *Equus burchelli*

**Family** Equidae

**Order** Perissodactyla

**Size** Length head/body: 7.2–8.2 ft (2.2–2.5 m); tail length: 18.5–22 in (47–56 cm); height at shoulder: up to 43–57 in (110–145 cm)

**Weight** 385–710 lb (175–322 kg)

**Key features** Deep-bodied, short-legged zebra; thick, erect mane; black stripes broader than in other species, especially on rump, and do not always extend onto belly and legs; stripes sometimes interspersed with pale-brown lines

**Habits** Social: lives in nonterritorial, single-male harems or bachelor groups; active day and night

**Breeding** Single young born after gestation period of 360–396 days. Weaned at 7–11 months; females sexually mature at 16–22 months, males from 4 years. May live up to 40 years in captivity, usually many fewer in the wild

**Voice** Typical horse calls; snorts, gasps, squeals

**Diet** Mostly grass; some shrubs and flowering plants; shoots, twigs, and leaves of trees

**Habitat** Savanna and lightly wooded or scrubby grassland

**Distribution** Southern and eastern Africa outside forested and developed land

**Status** Population: 750,000; IUCN Data Deficient. Declining; protected in several national parks

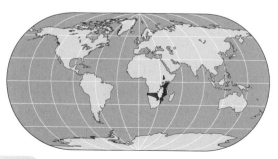

# Mongolian Wild Horse

**Common name**
Mongolian wild
horse (wild horse, Przewalski's horse, takh)

**Scientific name** *Equus przewalskii*
(*Equus caballus przewalskii*)

**Family** Equidae

**Order** Perissodactyla

**Size** Length head/body: 7.2–9 ft (2.2–2.8 m); tail length: 39 in (100 cm); height at shoulder: up to 4.3 ft (1.3 m)

**Weight** 440–660 lb (200–300 kg)

**Key features** Stocky, heavy-looking horse with a short, thick neck, erect, dark mane, and no forelock; tail dark with long hairs only on lower part; fur beige-brown with dark dorsal stripe and pale muzzle; winter coat shaggy

**Habits** Social; active by day; nonterritorial; shy and nervous: often has to be tranquilized before handling

**Breeding** Single foal born in spring at least every 2 years after gestation period of 11 months. Weaned at 18–24 months; sexually mature at 2–4 years, although males do not breed until they are mature enough to defend a harem. May live up to 38 years in captivity

**Voice** Typical horse calls; grunts, squeals

**Diet** Grass and other vegetation

**Habitat** Extensive, open, dry grasslands

**Distribution** Formerly in southwestern Mongolia

**Status** Population: about 1,500 (all captive bred); IUCN Extinct in the Wild; CITES I

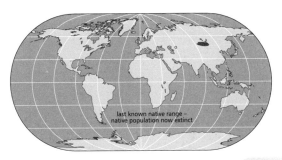

last known native range – native population now extinct

**125**

# Asian Wild Ass

**Common name** Asian wild ass
(onager, kulan, khur, kiang)

**Scientific name** *Equus hemionus*

**Family** Equidae

**Order** Perissodactyla

**Size** Length head/body: 6.5–8.2 ft (2–2.5 m); tail length: 12–19 in (30–49 cm); height at shoulder: up to 39–56 in (100–142 cm)

**Weight** 440–570 lb (200–258 kg)

**Key features** Large ass with grayish-beige to reddish-brown coat, pale on legs and belly, with dark dorsal stripe; short mane; hooves broader than in other asses

**Habits** Males territorial; large herds form occasionally to feed or migrate, but do not last; feeding mostly diurnal

**Breeding** Single young born every other year in summer after gestation period of 11 months. Weaned at 12–18 months; females sexually mature at 2 years, males at 3 years. Kiangs may live up to 26 years in captivity, other Asian asses a maximum of 23 years, probably fewer in the wild

**Voice** Grunts, squeals, and braying calls (males only)

**Diet** Grass and other low-growing vegetation

**Habitat** Desert and arid grassland

**Distribution** Middle East and central Asia

**Status** Population: probably fewer than 100,000; IUCN Vulnerable; CITES I and II (various species and subspecies). Declining species

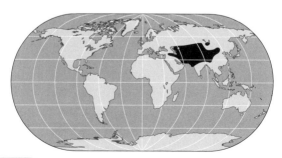

# Brazilian Tapir

**Common name** Brazilian tapir (South American tapir)

**Scientific name** *Tapirus terrestris*

**Family** Tapiridae

**Order** Perissodactyla

**Size** Length head/body: up to 7.2 ft (2.2 m); tail length: 3 in (8 cm); height at shoulder: 30–42 in (77–108 cm)

**Weight** Up to 550 lb (250 kg)

**Key features** Bulky animal with narrow front end, rounded rump, slender legs, and short tail; head tapers to short snout; ears oval and erect, eyes small; coat sparse with narrow mane; 4 toes on front feet, 3 on hind feet

**Habits** Mainly nocturnal; solitary and aggressive to other tapirs, but nonterritorial; swims and dives well; wallows in mud

**Breeding** Single young (occasionally twins) born after gestation period of 13 months. Weaned at about 12 months; sexually mature at 2–3 years. May live up to 35 years in captivity, probably many fewer in the wild

**Voice** Loud squeals, low-frequency clicks and whistling sounds

**Diet** Mainly grass, leaves, and shoots of terrestrial and aquatic plants; also twigs, bark, and fruit; sometimes raids crops such as rice and corn

**Habitat** Humid forest with dense vegetation and permanent sources of water

**Distribution** Northern and central South America east of Andes

**Status** Population: probably several thousand; IUCN Lower Risk: near threatened; CITES II. Declining due to habitat loss and hunting

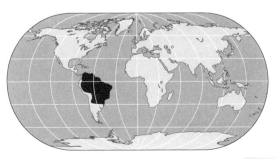

# Common Hippopotamus

**Common name** Common hippopotamus (hippo)

**Scientific name**
*Hippopotamus amphibius*

**Family** Hippopotamidae

**Order** Artiodactyla

**Size** Length head/body: 10.8-11.3 ft (3.3-3.5 m); tail length: 14-20 in (35-50 cm); height at shoulder: 4.6 ft (1.4 m)

**Weight** Male 1.4-2.8 tons (1.3-2.5 tonnes); female 1.2 tons (1 tonne)

**Key features** Bulky body with broad, expanded muzzle; skin naked and gray-brown to blue-black on upper body; lower parts pinkish; 4-toed feet; lower canine teeth enlarged as tusks

**Habits** Mostly nocturnal; rests in water by day, grazes on savanna grassland by night

**Breeding** One calf born, usually in water, after gestation period of about 240 days. Weaned at 6-8 months; females sexually mature at 7-15 years, males at 6-13 years. May live about 49 years in captivity, 45 in the wild

**Voice** Squeals, honks, bellows, deep rumbles; loud "ho-ho-ho"

**Diet** Savanna grasses, but some commercial crops (mainly rice) taken in agricultural regions

**Habitat** Short grasslands; rivers, lakes, and muddy wallows

**Distribution** West, central, East, and southern Africa

**Status** Population: 174,000; IUCN Vulnerable (subspecies *H. a. tschadensis*); CITES II. Species as a whole not currently threatened, although numbers are declining

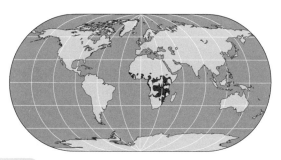

# Wild Boar

**Common name**
Wild boar

**Scientific name** *Sus scrofa*

**Family** Suidae

**Order** Artiodactyla

**Size** Length head/body: 35–71 in (90–180 cm); tail length: 12–16 in (30–40 cm); height at shoulder: 24–35 in (60–90 cm)

**Weight** 110–440 lb (50–200 kg). Male heavier than female; heaviest individuals occur in north and often result from breeding with feral domestic pigs

**Key features** Stocky body with short neck and large, long head; brown-gray bristly coat with short, dense winter coat; relatively small tusks

**Habits** Active during daytime and twilight; wallows to keep cool in hot climates

**Breeding** Three to 10 (generally 5–6) young born after gestation period of about 115 days. Weaned at 3–4 months; sexually mature at 18 months. May live up to 20 years in captivity, 8–10 in the wild

**Voice** Squeals and grunts

**Diet** Variety of plant and animal matter, including acorns, roots, tubers, green plants, earthworms, grasshoppers, and snails; occasionally carrion and small rodents

**Habitat** Broad-leaved woodlands

**Distribution** Europe, North Africa, Asia, Sumatra, Japan, and Taiwan. Introduced into Australia, New Zealand, and North and South America

**Status** Common, widespread; often a pest in agricultural areas

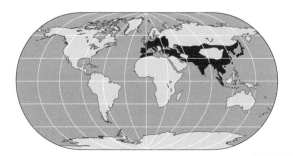

# Warthog

**Common name** Warthog

**Scientific name** *Phacochoerus africanus*

**Family** Suidae

**Order** Artiodactyla

**Size** Length head/body: 43–53 in (110–135 cm); tail length: 16 in (40 cm); height at shoulder: 22–34 in (55–85 cm)

**Weight** 110–220 lb (50–100 kg)

**Key features** Relatively long-legged, short-necked pig; prominent curved tusks and facial warts; tough snout for unearthing food; gray skin nearly naked with sparse black hairs on body and paler bristles around the jaws

**Habits** Generally active throughout day, sleeps in burrows at night; social: closely related females form clans; males join clans during breeding season, but are otherwise solitary

**Breeding** Two to 3 (but up to 8) piglets born after gestation period of 170–175 days. Weaned at 6 months; sexually mature at 1.5 years. May live up to 18 years in the wild, not usually kept in captivity

**Voice** Grunts, squeals, and growls; males make mumbling noises during courtship

**Diet** Grass, roots, berries, bark of young trees, and occasionally other animal remains

**Habitat** Usually dry, open wooded areas

**Distribution** African savannas

**Status** Population: abundant; IUCN Endangered (subspecies *P. a. aeliani*). Eliminated from areas of intensive farming; elsewhere abundant, especially in national parks

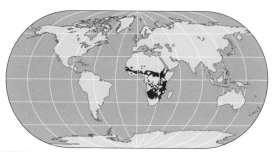

# Babirusa

**Common name** Babirusa

**Scientific name** *Babyrousa babyrussa*

**Family** Suidae

**Order** Artiodactyla

**Size** Length head/body: 33–41 in (85–105 cm); tail length: 11–13 in (27–32 cm); height at shoulder: 25–31 in (65–80 cm)

**Weight** Up to 220 lb (100 kg)

**Key features** Small- to medium-sized pig with loose-fitting, brownish-gray skin; males have 2 pairs of large, upward-pointing tusks; upper pair grow through top of muzzle and curl back toward forehead; females have 4 mammae

**Habits** Diurnal; lives in small groups; shy, active, and nimble; wallows in mud, swims well

**Breeding** Litters of 1–2 young born in spring after gestation period of 5 months. Weaning starts at 2 weeks; sexually mature at 6–12 months. May live up to 24 years in captivity, probably fewer in the wild

**Voice** Piggy grunts and groaning sounds

**Diet** Leaves, fallen fruit, and nuts

**Habitat** Wet forests and swampy areas

**Distribution** Sulawesi and a few small Indonesian islands

**Status** Population: fewer than 4,000; IUCN Vulnerable; CITES I. Declining due to habitat loss and poaching

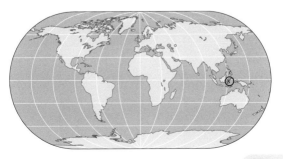

# Collared Peccary

**Common name** Collared peccary (javelina)

**Scientific name** *Tayassu tajacu* (*Pecari tajacu*)

**Family** Tayassuidae

**Order** Artiodactyla

**Size** Length head/body: 29–39 in (75–100 cm); tail length: 1–2 in (2–6 cm); height at shoulder: up to 17–20 in (44–50 cm)

**Weight** 31–77 lb (14–35 kg)

**Key features** Smallish, piglike animal with bristly, dark-gray fur and white collar; head large with bulging forehead; legs slender; 2 weight-bearing toes (hind feet have third vestigial toe); sharp, downward-pointing tusks

**Habits** Lives in territorial groups; nocturnal; runs quickly; bathes in mud and sand wallows

**Breeding** Litters of 1–4 (usually 2–3) young born after gestation period of 4–5 months. Weaned at 7–10 weeks; females sexually mature at 9 months, males at 11 months. May live up to 24 years in captivity, 16 in the wild

**Voice** Wide range of grunts, snorts, clicks, barks, and growls

**Diet** Mainly vegetarian: fruit, berries, plant roots, bulbs, and tubers; invertebrates such as insect larvae; small vertebrates, including snakes

**Habitat** Diverse; dry cactus scrub and semidesert to tropical rain forest; needs shelter during day

**Distribution** Southern U.S. (Arizona, Texas, and New Mexico); Central and South America as far south as northern Argentina

**Status** Population: abundant; CITES II. Declining, especially in Central and South America; hunted within game laws

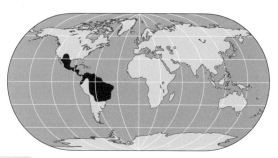

# Dromedary Camel

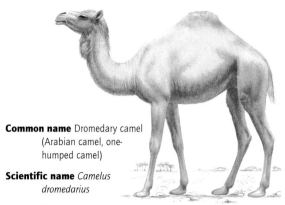

**Common name** Dromedary camel (Arabian camel, one-humped camel)

**Scientific name** *Camelus dromedarius*

**Family** Camelidae

**Order** Artiodactyla

**Size** Length head/body: 7.5–11.4 ft (2.3–3.5 m); tail length: 14–21 in (35–55 cm); height to top of hump: 5.9–7.5 ft (1.8–2.3 m)

**Weight** 660–1,540 lb (300–698 kg)

**Key features** Tall; long neck and legs; single large dorsal hump; tail thin and hairy; head small, with small, furry ears, large, thickly lashed eyes, closable nostrils, and split upper lip; fur short and woolly, pale beige to dark brown

**Habits** Active during the day in small herds; not territorial and generally nonaggressive

**Breeding** Single calf (twins rare) born every other year at most at any time of year after gestation period of 15 months (births peak in the rainy season). Weaned at 12–18 months; females sexually mature at 3 years; males take 6 years to reach size at which they can defend mates. May live up to 50 years in captivity, similar in the wild

**Voice** Rumbling moans and grunts

**Diet** Any desert plant, including those with high salt content

**Habitat** Deserts

**Distribution** Originally from Arabian Peninsula; feral and semiwild populations also in North Africa, Asia, and central Australia

**Status** Population: may exceed 19 million; IUCN Extinct in the Wild. Domesticated

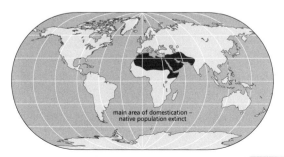

main area of domestication – native population extinct

# Bactrian Camel

**Common name** Bactrian camel (two-humped camel)

**Scientific name** *Camelus bactrianus* (*Camelus ferus*)

**Family** Camelidae

**Order** Artiodactyla

**Size** Length head/body: 7.5–11 ft (2.3–3.5 m); tail length: 14–22 in (35–55 cm); height to top of hump: 6.2–7.5 ft (1.9–2.3 m)

**Weight** 990–1,430 lb (450–650 kg)

**Key features** Long-legged, long-necked animal; 2 tall humps on back; head small with small, round ears, large eyes, and split upper lip; feet broad with 2 toes and soft pads

**Habits** Social: lives in herds; nonterritorial; active by day

**Breeding** Single calf born every other year in spring after gestation period of 12–14 months. Weaned at 12–18 months; sexually mature at 3 years. May live up to 50 years in captivity, similar in the wild

**Voice** Grunts and grumbling sounds

**Diet** Mostly plant material

**Habitat** Steppe, desert, and rocky scrublands

**Distribution** Wild specimens restricted to northwestern China and Mongolia

**Status** Population: 2 million (fewer than 1,000 truly wild); IUCN Endangered (wild); CITES I. International protection measures do not include domestic animals

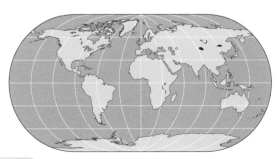

# Llama

**Common name**
Llama

**Scientific name** *Lama glama*

**Family** Camelidae

**Order** Artiodactyla

**Size** Length head/body: 47–88 in (120–225 cm); tail length: 6–10 in (15–25 cm); height at shoulder: up to 43–47 in (109–119 cm)

**Weight** 286–342 lb (130–155 kg)

**Key features** Long-legged, long-necked animal with short, inconspicuous tail; coat thick and woolly, usually beige to dark brown, sometimes pale with blotches; fur shorter and finer on head and legs; head small and sheeplike, with split upper lip; ears large, long, and mobile; feet smaller than those of camels, with 2 small hooves

**Habits** Feral and free-living animals live in groups dominated by single territorial male

**Breeding** Single calf born November–February after gestation period of 11–11.5 months. Weaned at 6–8 months; sexually mature at 1 year. May live at least 10 years in captivity, similar for feral populations

**Voice** Rumbling growls when angry or upset

**Diet** Grasses; leaves of other plants, trees, and shrubs

**Habitat** Grassland and scrub at high altitudes up to 13,000 ft (4,000 m)

**Distribution** Most live under domestication in Andes region of South America

**Status** Population: about 3,700,000; IUCN Extinct in the Wild. Domesticated

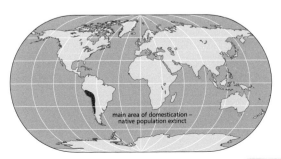

main area of domestication –
native population extinct

# Vicuña

**Common name** Vicuña

**Scientific name** *Vicugna vicugna*

**Family** Camelidae

**Order** Artiodactyla

**Size** Length head/ body: 4.2–6.2 ft (1.3–1.9 m); tail length: 6–10 in (15–25 cm); height at shoulder: up to 27.5–43 in (70–110 cm)

**Weight** 77–133 lb (35–60 kg)

**Key features** Slender, llamalike animal with long neck, small head, and long, thin legs; split upper lip; tail short and shaggy; coat of fine wool; reddish-brown on head and body, thick white "mane" on chest

**Habits** Social, territorial; active by day, but seldom travels far

**Breeding** Single young born February–March after gestation period of 11–11.5 months. Weaned at 6–8 months; sexually mature at 2 years. May live up to 28 years in captivity, 20 in the wild

**Voice** Whistling alarm call; various hoarse contact sounds; male has musical mating call known as "orgling"

**Diet** Grasses and other low-growing herbs

**Habitat** Alpine grasslands (puna) of Andes Mountains from 12,000–15,750 ft (3,700–4,800 m)

**Distribution** Peru; also parts of Bolivia, Argentina, and Chile

**Status** Population: 250,000; IUCN Lower Risk: conservation dependent; CITES I. Recovering from all-time low of 6,000 animals in late 1960–70s

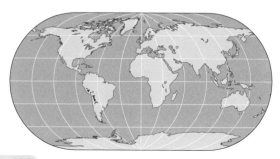

# Moose

**Common name**
Moose (elk in Europe)

**Scientific name** *Alces alces*

**Family** Cervidae

**Order** Artiodactyla

**Size** Length head/body: 5–9.5 ft (1.6–2.9 m); tail length: 2.8–4 in (7–10 cm); height at shoulder: male 6–7.5 ft (1.8–2.3 m); female 5–5.6 ft (1.5–1.7 m)

**Weight** Male 700–1,760 lb (317–800 kg); female 605–825 lb (274–374 kg)

**Key features** Tall with long, thin legs; elongated head; fleshy "bell" hangs from throat; antlers may span 5 ft (1.5 m)

**Habits** Generally solitary, but herds may form in winter; often enters water, swims well

**Breeding** Single calf or twins (occasionally triplets) born May–June after gestation period of 240–250 days. Weaned at 5 months; sexually mature at 1 year. May live up to 27 years in captivity, 20 (females) or 15 (males) in the wild

**Voice** Deep lowing (males); muffled cough

**Diet** Tree shoots and twigs; large herbs, leaves, and aquatic plants in summer

**Habitat** Woodland and nearby open country

**Distribution** North America and northern Eurasia; introduced to New Zealand

**Status** Population: around 1 million in North America and 1 million in Eurasia; IUCN Lower Risk: near threatened (Siberian subspecies). Generally abundant and widespread

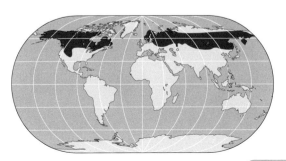

# Reindeer/ Caribou

**Common name** Reindeer (Europe), caribou (North America)

**Scientific name** *Rangifer tarandus*

**Family** Cervidae

**Order** Artiodactyla

**Size** Length head/body:
6.2–7.2 ft (1.9–2.2 m); tail length: 4–6 in (10–15 cm); height at shoulder: 42–50 in (107–127 cm). Female generally 10–15% smaller

**Weight** 200–600 lb (91–272 kg)

**Key features** Large dark-brown deer, appears gray in winter; chest and legs darker than body, neck paler; patches of white on rump, tail, and above hooves; antlers in both sexes

**Habits** Lives in herds; moves seasonally to find food

**Breeding** Single calf, rarely twins, born May–June after gestation period of 210–240 days. Weaned at 1 month; sexually mature at 18–36 months. May live over 20 years in captivity, 15 in the wild (females), 10 (males)

**Voice** Series of grunting noises

**Diet** Lichens, sedges, grass, fungi; also browses leaves

**Habitat** Mainly Arctic tundra and forest edges

**Distribution** From Alaska through Canada to Greenland; Scandinavia through Europe and Russia to Sakhalin Island in North Pacific; introduced to Iceland, South Georgia, and other islands

**Status** Population: several million, including many semidomesticated animals in Europe; IUCN Endangered (subspecies *R. t. pearyi*)

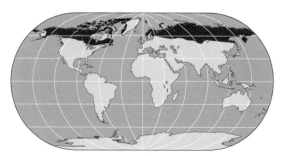

# Elk

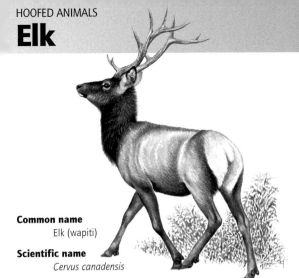

**Common name**
Elk (wapiti)

**Scientific name**
*Cervus canadensis*

**Family** Cervidae

**Order** Artiodactyla

**Size** Length head/body: male
6.5–8 ft (2–2.5 m); female
6–7.5 ft (1.9–2.3 m); tail
length: 3–7.5 in (8–19 cm);
height at shoulder: 4.3–5 ft
(1.3–1.5 m)

**Weight** Male 392–1,096 lb (178–497 kg); female 377–644 lb
(171–292 kg)

**Key features** Coat brownish-red in summer, paler in winter; pale
rump patch, dark-brown mane; antlers up to 5 ft (1.5 m)
long (males only)

**Habits** Gregarious: lives in single-sex herds for most of year;
males fight for mating rights

**Breeding** Single calf (twins rare) born late May or early June
after gestation period of 249–262 days. Weaned at
about 2.5 months; sexually mature at 28 months. May
live up to 25 years in captivity, about 15 in the wild

**Voice** Barks, squeals; "bugle" noise (males)

**Diet** Grasses, forbs, bushes, and trees

**Habitat** Grassland, forest edge, and mountains, often near water

**Distribution** Western North America and parts of Asia;
introduced to New Zealand

**Status** Population: about 1 million

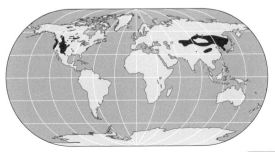

# Red Deer

**Common name** Red deer

**Scientific name** *Cervus elaphus*

**Family** Cervidae

**Order** Artiodactyla

**Size** Length head/body: 5.6–8.5 ft (1.7–2.6 m); tail length: 6–8 in (15–20 cm); height at shoulder: about 47 in (120 cm)

**Weight** Male up to 560 lb (254 kg); female up to 330 lb (150 kg)

**Key features** Large brown deer with creamy-orange rump patch; no dark markings; branched antlers in male

**Habits** Mainly active at dawn and dusk; lives in herds; gathers in groups to breed in early fall

**Breeding** Single calf, occasionally twins, born after gestation period of 225–245 days. Weaned at 4–7 months; sexually mature at 1–3 years. May live 27 years in captivity, up to 25 in the wild, but usually only half that

**Voice** Males roar loudly on breeding grounds; females and calves make bleating noises

**Diet** Leaves and shoots from wide range of trees and shrubs; grass and sedges in winter

**Habitat** Prefers woodlands, but also found in parks and open hillsides; migrates above tree line in summer in Scandinavia

**Distribution** Widespread in Central Europe; scattered in Scandinavia, Mediterranean countries, Turkey, and east to Tibet; introduced in Australia, New Zealand, Texas, and South America

**Status** Population: abundant; generally increasing

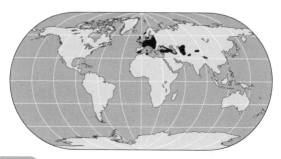

HOOFED ANIMALS

# Mule Deer

**Common name** Mule deer (black-tailed deer)

**Scientific name** *Odocoileus hemionus*

**Family** Cervidae

**Order** Artiodactyla

**Size** Length head/body: 5–7 ft (1.5–2 m); tail length: 4.5–9 in (11–23 cm); height at shoulder: male 31–42 in (80–106 cm). Female smaller than male

**Weight** 250–300 lb (113–136 kg)

**Key features** Medium-sized deer with large, mobile ears; coat rusty red in summer, brownish-gray in winter; whitish face, throat, and rump; black bar on chin and v-shaped or triangular patch on forehead; tail white with black tip or all-black

**Habits** Active mainly at dusk and dawn; moderately sociable: lives in small, loose herds; bouncing gait ("stotting") when fleeing predators

**Breeding** Usually twins born after gestation period of 203 days. Weaned at 4 months; sexually mature at 16 months, but males breed later. May live up to 24 years in captivity, 10–12 in the wild (females), 8 (males)

**Voice** Bleats (in fawns); snorts, grunts, and barks

**Diet** Grasses, sedges, forbs, bushes, and trees

**Habitat** Varied; usually open forest, bush, or scrubland; often steep or rough terrain

**Distribution** Western North America from Alaska to Mexico east to Nebraska and the Dakotas; introduced to Kauai (Hawaii) and Argentina

**Status** Population: at least 3 million; IUCN Endangered (Cedros Island subspecies)

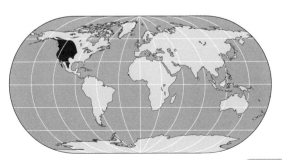

# Roe Deer

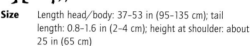

**Common name** Roe deer

**Scientific name** *Capreolus capreolus*

**Family** Cervidae

**Order** Artiodactyla

**Size** Length head/body: 37–53 in (95–135 cm); tail length: 0.8–1.6 in (2–4 cm); height at shoulder: about 25 in (65 cm)

**Weight** 35–77 lb (16–35 kg)

**Key features** Medium-sized deer; bright chestnut in summer, gray-brown in winter; distinctive black nose and white tail patch (but actual tail almost invisible); antlers short and spiky, with rough, knobby surface and few prongs

**Habits** Generally solitary and territorial; active at any time of day, particularly after dark

**Breeding** Kids (usually twins) born early summer after gestation period of 290 days (including delayed implantation). Weaned at 2 months; sexually mature at 1–2 years. May live 20 years in captivity, 7–8 in the wild, but sometimes up to 15

**Voice** Hoarse bark when alarmed

**Diet** Leaves from wide range of trees and shrubs; also crops and garden plants

**Habitat** Dense shrubbery and undergrowth, often venturing into open fields to feed

**Distribution** Most of western Europe through Russia and Turkey to China and Korea

**Status** Population: abundant. Common and widespread; on the increase in many parts of Europe

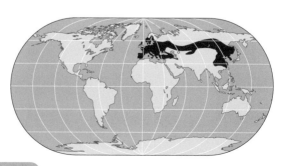

# Fallow Deer

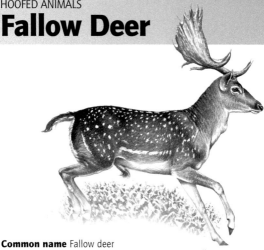

**Common name** Fallow deer

**Scientific name** *Dama dama*

**Family** Cervidae

**Order** Artiodactyla

**Size** Length head/body: 4–5.5 ft (1–1.7 m); tail length: 6–7.5 in (16–19 cm); height at shoulder: about 33 in (85 cm)

**Weight** Male 140–227 lb (63–103 kg); female 64–119 lb (29–54 kg)

**Key features** Unusual flat antlers; colors range from white to almost black, but typically brown with white spots; tail usually black on top, with white patch edged with black

**Habits** Lives in small herds; often mainly nocturnal, especially where it invades farmland; normally spends day hidden among trees or shrubs

**Breeding** Single fawn born in June after gestation period of 7–8 months. Weaned at 4 months; sexually mature at 18 months, but males breed much later. May live 20 years in captivity, usually many fewer in the wild

**Voice** Young bleat; bucks groan during rut

**Diet** Grazes grass or browses trees and bushes

**Habitat** Woodland, farmland, and deer parks

**Distribution** Scattered areas in most of Europe; southern Turkey east to Iran; introduced to many countries

**Status** Population: abundant; IUCN Endangered (Iranian population only). A common animal

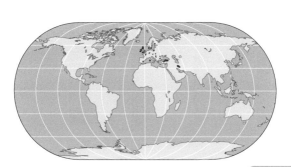

# Muntjac

**Common name**
Muntjac (Reeves's muntjac, Chinese muntjac, barking deer)

**Scientific name** *Muntiacus reevesi*

**Family** Cervidae

**Order** Artiodactyla

**Size** Length head/body: 35–39 in (90–100 cm); tail length: about 6 in (15 cm); height at shoulder: 18–20 in (45–52 cm)

**Weight** 26–33 lb (12–15 kg)

**Key features** Small deer with hunched appearance; bright chestnut color with dark "eyebrow" markings; small antlers: single spikes on top of furry bases that are almost as tall as the antlers themselves

**Habits** Active day or night; skulking and solitary

**Breeding** Single young born (twins rare) after gestation period of 7 months. Weaned at about 3 months; sexually mature at 9–10 months. May live up to 19 years in captivity, at least 16 in the wild

**Voice** Loud barks when alarmed

**Diet** Nibbles leaves from shrubs and low-growing trees; also nuts and fruit; grass when favored food not available

**Habitat** Dense undergrowth and thickets in deciduous and conifer forests

**Distribution** Southern China and Taiwan; introduced to Britain and now widespread there

**Status** Population: about 700,000 in Asia and 50,000 in Britain. Increasingly scarce in its native home, but expanding in range and population in Britain

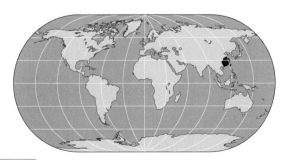

# Himalayan Musk Deer

**Common name** Himalayan musk deer

**Scientific name** *Moschus chrysogaster*

**Family** Moschidae

**Order** Artiodactyla

**Size** Length head/body: 27.5–39 in (70–100 cm); tail length: 1–2.5 in (2.5–6 cm); height at shoulder: 20–21 in (51–53 cm)

**Weight** 24–31 lb (11–14 kg). Female usually heavier than male

**Key features** Generally dark brown; hunched back with shoulders lower than rump; coat mottled with gray, spotted with white when young; no antlers, but large tusks in males

**Habits** Solitary; skulking

**Breeding** One, sometimes 2, fawns born May–June after gestation period of 6.5 months. Weaned at 6 weeks; sexually mature at 18 months. May live up to 20 years in captivity, fewer in the wild

**Voice** Normally silent, but hisses when disturbed and screams when injured

**Diet** Mostly leaves and lichens from low-growing trees and shrubs; also conifer needles and bark; in summer a wide range of herbaceous plants; also some grasses

**Habitat** Mountain forests of dwarf rhododendrons and dense thickets

**Distribution** Himalayas, western China, and Tibet

**Status** Population: still many thousands; IUCN Lower Risk: near threatened; CITES II. Some deer still killed for their musk despite ban on trade; forest clearance also a problem

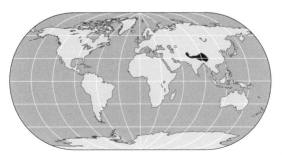

# Giraffe

**Common name** Giraffe

**Scientific name** *Giraffa camelopardalis*

**Family** Giraffidae

**Order** Artiodactyla

**Size** Length head/body: 11.5–16 ft (3.5–4.8 m); tail length: 30–43 in (76–110 cm); height at shoulder: 8.2–12 ft (2.5–3.7 m)

**Weight** Male 1,760–4,250 lb (800–1,930 kg); female 1,210–2,600 lb (550–1,180 kg)

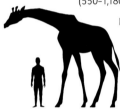

**Key features** Tall with long, flexible, maned neck and long, thin legs; body slopes down from shoulders to rump; both sexes have short horns; short coat has a pattern of chestnut-brown patches on creamy-white background

**Habits** Lives in loose groups; active both day and night; hardly sleeps

**Breeding** One calf born after gestation period of 453–464 days. Weaned at 12 months; females sexually mature at about 3.5 years, males at about 4.5 years. May live up to 36 years in captivity, 25 in the wild

**Voice** Grunts and snorts; calves bleat

**Diet** Leaves plucked from trees and shrubs, in particular from acacia, mimosa, and wild apricot trees

**Habitat** Open woodland and wooded grassland

**Distribution** Africa south of the Sahara, up to 6,560 ft (2,000 m) above sea level

**Status** Population: relatively abundant; IUCN Lower Risk: conservation dependent

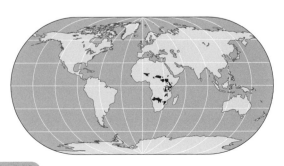

# Okapi

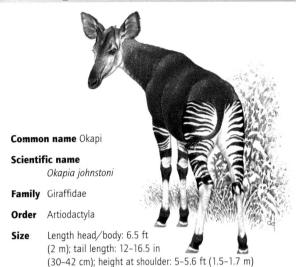

**Common name** Okapi

**Scientific name**
Okapia johnstoni

**Family** Giraffidae

**Order** Artiodactyla

**Size** Length head/body: 6.5 ft
(2 m); tail length: 12–16.5 in
(30–42 cm); height at shoulder: 5–5.6 ft (1.5–1.7 m)

**Weight** 440–550 lb (200–250 kg)

**Key features** Dark chestnut-brown coat tinged
with purple and red; white face with brown
nose, forehead, and ears; legs and rump
striped with white; short horns on head of
both sexes, larger on male

**Habits** Lives alone or in temporary
groups; diurnal; secretive and elusive

**Breeding** One calf born after gestation period of 427–457 days.
Weaned at 6 months; females sexually mature at 19
months, males later. May live at least 33 years in
captivity, 15–20 in the wild

**Voice** Coughs, snorts, and piping sounds; female bellows to
attract males, and males make soft moans during
courtship; young bleat

**Diet** Leaves, fruit, and seeds

**Habitat** Dense, low undergrowth in equatorial rain forest

**Distribution** Only in northern, central, and eastern Democratic
Republic of Congo near DRC-Uganda border

**Status** Population: estimated at 10,000–20,000; IUCN Lower
Risk: near threatened. Thought to be rare; has been a
protected species since 1933

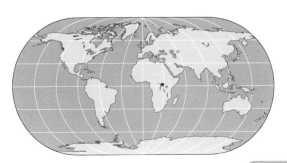

# American Bison

**Common name** American bison (buffalo)

**Scientific name** *Bison bison*

**Family** Bovidae

**Order** Artiodactyla

**Size** Length head/body: male 10–12 ft (3–3.8 m); female 7–10 ft (2.1–3.2 m); tail length: 17–35 in (43–90 cm); height at shoulder: up to 6.2 ft (1.9 m)

**Weight** Male 1,000–2,000 lb (454–907 kg); female 790–1,200 lb (358–544 kg)

**Key features** Large, oxlike animal with head held low and large hump over the shoulders; forelegs, neck, and shoulders covered in long, dark-brown hair; both sexes have horns

**Habits** Lives in large herds that migrate across open grasslands; feeds mostly early and late in day

**Breeding** Single calf born May–August after gestation period of 9–10 months. Weaned at about 6 months; sexually mature at 2–3 years. May live up to 40 years in captivity, up to 25 in the wild

**Voice** Snorts, grunts, and cowlike noises; bulls bellow and roar during the rut

**Diet** Mostly grass; also sedges, wild flowers, shrubs such as willow and sagebrush; lichens and mosses in winter

**Habitat** Prairies, sagebrush, and open wooded areas

**Distribution** Midwestern U.S. and Canada

**Status** Population: 200,000–500,000; IUCN Lower Risk: conservation dependent; Endangered (subspecies *B. b. athabascae*); CITES II

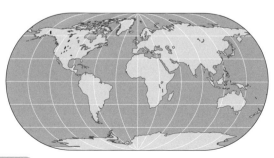

# African Buffalo

**Common name** African buffalo

**Scientific name** *Syncerus caffer*

**Family** Bovidae

**Order** Artiodactyla

**Size** Length head/body: 8–11 ft (2.4–3.4 m); tail length: 30–43 in (75–110 cm); height at shoulder: 4.6–5.5 ft (1.4–1.7 m)

**Weight** 550–1,870 lb (250–848 kg). Male more heavily built than female

**Key features** Huge black or brown oxlike creature; hairy ears and massive horns that meet on top of the forehead to form a heavy "boss"; reddish forest form is smaller

**Habits** Lives in herds, sometimes of only a few animals, but many hundreds may congregate seasonally in good feeding areas

**Breeding** One calf normally produced every 2 years after gestation period of 11 months. Weaned at about 1 year; sexually mature at 3–5 years. May live over 29 years in captivity, 18 in the wild

**Voice** Generally silent

**Diet** Grass; wide variety of swamp vegetation

**Habitat** Savanna woodland and open grassy glades; usually near water and often wallows in mud; forest form lives under continuous tree cover

**Distribution** Widely dispersed across West, central, and East Africa south of Sahara

**Status** Population: probably at least 100,000; IUCN Lower Risk: conservation dependent. Common, but severely reduced in places due to disease, habitat loss, and hunting

# Yak

**Common name** Yak

**Scientific name** *Bos grunniens*

**Family** Bovidae

**Order** Artiodactyla

**Size** Length head/body: up to 11 ft (3.3 m); tail length: about 20 in (50 cm); height at shoulder: up to 6.6 ft (2 m)

**Weight** Male 670–2,200 lb (300–1,000 kg). Female about 60% smaller

**Key features** Massive, shaggy, oxlike animal with high, humped shoulders and low-slung head; dense woolly hair almost reaching ground; dark brown to black with white around muzzle; both sexes have very long curved horns

**Habits** Lives in small herds, gathering into larger groups in summer where food is available

**Breeding** Single calf born in June every other year after gestation period of 255–304 days. Weaned at 1 year; sexually mature at 6–8 years. May live up to 25 years in captivity, similar in the wild

**Voice** Deep grunts, but generally silent

**Diet** Wiry tufts of grass, shrubs, herbs, and lichens

**Habitat** Alpine tundra and steppe 13,000–19,680 ft (4,000–6,000 m); above snow line in summer

**Distribution** Remote areas of Tibetan plateau; Xinjiang and Qinghai (northwestern China); eastern Kashmir (India)

**Status** Population: probably fewer than 10,000 in the wild; IUCN Vulnerable; CITES I since 1975

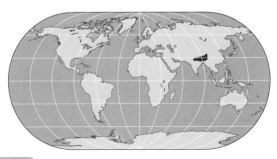

# Giant Eland

**Common name** Giant eland
(Lord Derby's eland)

**Scientific name** *Taurotragus derbianus*

**Family** Bovidae

**Order** Artiodactyla

**Size** Length head/body: male 8–10 ft (2.4–3.2 m); female
7–8 ft (2.1–2.4 m); tail length: 22–31 in (55–78 cm);
height at shoulder: male 5–6 ft (1.5–1.8 m); female
4.6–5.2 ft (1.4–1.6 m)

**Weight** Male 990–2,000 lb (450–907 kg); female 660–1,100 lb
(300–500 kg)

**Key features** Large, chestnut-brown antelope with 12–15 vertical
white stripes on flanks; both sexes have long, twisted
horns; raised shoulder hump and prominent dewlap

**Habits** Found in herds of up to 60 individuals but more often
15–25; males often solitary; shy and relatively docile

**Breeding** Single calf born after gestation period of 9 months.
Weaned at about 4 months; females sexually mature at
28 months, males at 18 months, but will not breed until
older. May live up to 25 years, not often kept in captivity

**Voice** Deep grunts, snorts, and moos

**Diet** Acacia and related trees such as *Isoberlinia*; also other
leaves, shoots, and grasses

**Habitat** Woodland and forested savannas generally in or close to
*Isoberlinia* woodlands

**Distribution** Fragmented across northern-central Africa

**Status** Population: unknown, probably only a few thousand

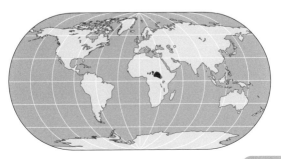

# Common Duiker

**Common name** Common duiker (bush duiker)

**Scientific name** *Sylvicapra grimmia*

**Family** Bovidae

**Order** Artiodactyla

**Size** Length head/body: male 28–41 in (70–105 cm); female 35–45 in (90–115 cm); tail length: 3–8 in (7–20 cm); height at shoulder: 18–28 in (45–70 cm)

**Weight** Male 24–46 lb (11–21 kg); female 26–55 lb (12–25 kg)

**Key features** Small antelope; face long with black band down midline to rounded, black nose; coat light gray to reddish-brown with white undersides; short, black tail with fluffy, white underside; slender, tapering horns (male only)

**Habits** Generally solitary; acute hearing; most active in early morning, late afternoon, and night; nocturnal in some areas due to disturbance

**Breeding** Usually a single lamb born after gestation period of about 7 months. Weaned at about 4–6 weeks; sexually mature at 8–9 months. May live about 14 years in captivity, 12 in the wild

**Voice** Alarm call is a nasal snort; bleats loudly if caught, otherwise relatively quiet

**Diet** Leaves, twigs, flowers, fruit, and seeds of trees and shrubs; roots and tubers; caterpillars and other insects; also frogs, lizards, small mammals, and chicks of ground-nesting birds

**Habitat** Prefers savannas and woodlands, but can live almost anywhere with enough food and cover; mountainous regions up to snow line

**Distribution** Suitable habitats across Africa south of Sahara

**Status** Population: abundant

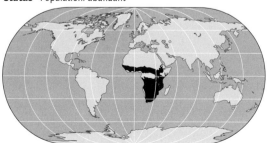

# Blue Wildebeest

**Common name**
Blue wildebeest (gnu)

**Scientific name**
*Connochaetes taurinus*

**Family** Bovidae

**Order** Artiodactyla

**Size** Length head/body: 5.6–8 ft (1.7–2.4 m); tail length: 24–39 in (60–100 cm); height at shoulder: 47–59 in (120–150 cm). Female shorter than male

**Weight** Male 363–638 lb (165–290 kg); female 308–572 lb (140–260 kg)

**Key features** Large, cowlike antelope; humped shoulders and deep neck; dark mane with fringe under neck that varies in color with subspecies

**Habits** Gregarious: found in herds of up to 20 or 30; herds of thousands form during migrations; active in early morning and late afternoon

**Breeding** Single calf born each year after gestation period of 8–8.5 months. Weaned at 9–12 months; females sexually mature at about 16 months, males breed later due to competition with larger rivals. May live over 21 years in captivity, similar in the wild

**Voice** Loud snorts and low moaning grunts

**Diet** Fresh growth of several species of grass

**Habitat** Savanna woodland and grassy plains

**Distribution** Found in 2 main areas of Africa: from Kenya to Mozambique; also from Zambia into South Africa

**Status** Population: hundreds of thousands. A common animal

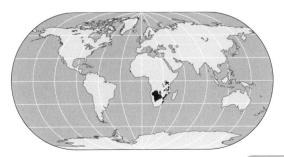

# Impala

**Common name** Impala

**Scientific name** *Aepyceros melampus*

**Family** Bovidae

**Order** Artiodactyla

**Size** Length head/body: 47–63 in (120–160 cm); tail length: 12–18 in (30–45 cm); height at shoulder: 30–37 in (75–95 cm)

**Weight** Male 99–176 lb (45–80 kg); female 88–132 lb (40–60 kg)

**Key features** Medium-sized, sleek, and lightly built antelope; long, slender legs; characteristic tuft of black hair on lower and rear edge of hind legs; upper body bright reddish-brown, sides fawn, underparts white; black-tipped ears, white eyebrows; male bears slender, ridged horns

**Habits** Gregarious; acute senses: explosion of activity when disturbed; social structure differs with season; mostly active during day, although avoids midday sun; some nocturnal activity

**Breeding** Generally single calf born each year after gestation period of 6.5 months. Weaned at 5–7 months; females sexually mature at 18 months, males at 12–13 months. May live about 15 years in captivity, similar in the wild

**Voice** High-pitched bark and snorts when alarmed; males roar, snort, and growl during rut

**Diet** Grass; also leaves and shoots; fruit and seeds of trees and bushes

**Habitat** Open woodlands and grasslands

**Distribution** Central and southeastern Africa from Kenya to South Africa; small population in southwestern Africa around southern Angola

**Status** Population: many thousands; IUCN Lower Risk: conservation dependent

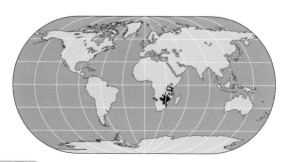

# Arabian Oryx

**Common name** Arabian oryx (white oryx)

**Scientific name** *Oryx leucoryx*

**Family** Bovidae

**Order** Artiodactyla

**Size** Length head/body: 5–5.2 ft (1.5–1.6 m); tail length: about 16–20 in (40–50 cm); height at shoulder: 31–39 in (80–100 cm)

**Weight** 140–155 lb (64–70 kg)

**Key features** Slender white antelope with straight horns (in both sexes); legs black, each with white band above hoof; face has dark markings

**Habits** Lives in small herds, wandering widely in search of sparse food

**Breeding** Single calf born at any time of year after gestation period of 240 days. Weaned at 4.5 months; sexually mature at about 3 years, but males unlikely to breed until older. May live up to 20 years in captivity, usually fewer in the wild

**Voice** Normally silent

**Diet** Grasses and desert shrubs

**Habitat** Dry, stony deserts

**Distribution** Formerly in Egypt, Iraq, Israel, Syria, United Arab Emirates, and Yemen. Now reintroduced to Jordan, Oman, and Saudi Arabia

**Status** Population: in excess of 2,000, but most in captivity; IUCN Endangered (wild populations formerly extinct, but reintroduced to Jordan, Oman, and Saudi Arabia); CITES I

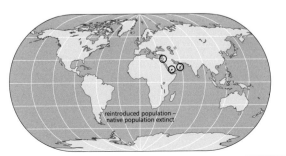

reintroduced population – native population extinct

# Waterbuck

**Common name**
Waterbuck

**Scientific name**
*Kobus ellipsiprymnus*

**Family** Bovidae

**Order** Artiodactyla

**Size** Length head/body: 6–7.5 ft (1.8–2.3 m); tail length: 13–16 in (33–40 cm); height at shoulder: 47–55 in (120–140 cm)

**Weight** Male 440–660 lb (200–300 kg); female 352–440 lb (160–200 kg)

**Key features** Robust antelope; coat long, coarse, and gray-brown to reddish; face dark with white chin; pale bands above eyes; shortish tail with dark tuft; broad white ring around rump; rounded ears; heavily ridged horns in males

**Habits** Social: herds usually 6–12 in number, but occasionally larger; adult males solitary and territorial; always lives close to water

**Breeding** Single calf born each year after gestation period of 8.5–9 months. Weaned at 6–9 months; females sexually mature at 18 months, males at 3 years but both breed later. May live about 18 years in captivity, similar in the wild

**Voice** Mothers bleat or snort when calling young

**Diet** Grasses, water plants, leaves, and shoots

**Habitat** Savanna, flood plains, woodland, and scrub; must be close to permanent source of water

**Distribution** Most of Africa south of Sahara as far south as northeastern South Africa

**Status** Population: low thousands; IUCN Lower Risk: conservation dependent. Declining

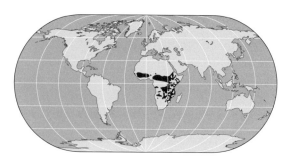

# Thomson's Gazelle

**Common name** Thomson's gazelle (tommy)

**Scientific name** *Gazella thomsoni*

**Family** Bovidae

**Order** Artiodactyla

**Size** Length head/body: 31–47 in (80–120 cm); tail length: 6–11 in (15–27 cm); height at shoulder: 22–32 in (55–82 cm)

**Weight** Male 44–77 lb (20–35 kg); female 33–55 lb (15–25 kg)

**Key features** Small, slender antelope; pale-brown coat, white underside; bold black band from shoulder to flank; white ring around eyes and boldly striped face; ridged, parallel horns curve backward with tips turning forward

**Habits** Migratory; lives in herds of 60 or more, led by a single female; mature males often solitary and territorial

**Breeding** Generally single offspring born up to twice a year after gestation period of 5–6 months. Weaned at 4–5 months; females sexually mature at about 9 months, males first breed at about 3 years. May live about 16 years in captivity, 10 in the wild

**Voice** Feeble bleats and whistles

**Diet** Fresh green grass in rains; herbs, foliage, and seeds of shrubs in dry season

**Habitat** Open savanna grasslands

**Distribution** Suitable habitats in Tanzania and Kenya; also isolated population in southern Sudan

**Status** Population: probably many thousands; IUCN Lower Risk: conservation dependent

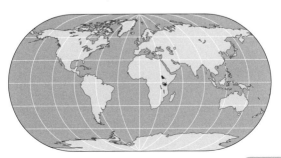

# Springbok

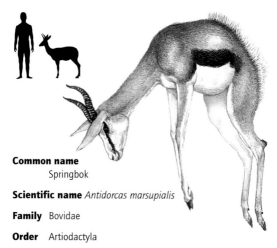

**Common name**
  Springbok

**Scientific name** *Antidorcas marsupialis*

**Family** Bovidae

**Order** Artiodactyla

**Size** Length head/body: 47–59 in (120–150 cm); tail length: 6–11 in (14–28 cm); height at shoulder: 27–35 in (68–90 cm)

**Weight** Male 66–130 lb (30–59 kg); female 44–95 lb (20–43 kg)

**Key features** Slender antelope; dark reddish-brown band separates cinnamon-brown upperparts from white underparts; fold of skin extends from back to rump, showing crest of white hair when opened; face white with reddish-brown stripe; long, narrow ears; short, ridged horns

**Habits** Gregarious: up to 1,500 individuals may move to fresh pastures during wet season; smaller herds in dry season

**Breeding** Usually single offspring born after gestation period of 6 months. Weaned at 4 months; females sexually mature at 7 months, males at about 12 months. May live up to 19 years in captivity, 10 in the wild

**Voice** Loud grunting bellows, high-pitched snorts, and bleats

**Diet** Fresh new grass; leaves and flowers of shrubs and trees; also digs for roots and bulbs

**Habitat** Prefers open habitats, arid plains, savanna, and semidesert habitats

**Distribution** Southern Angola, Namibia, Botswana, South Africa

**Status** Population: low thousands; IUCN Lower Risk: conservation dependent

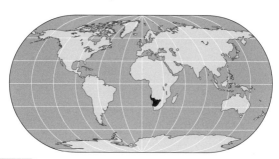

# American Bighorn Sheep

**Common name**
American bighorn sheep

**Scientific name** *Ovis canadensis*

**Family** Bovidae

**Order** Artiodactyla

**Size** Length head/body: male 5.5–6.2 ft (1.7–1.9 m); female 4.9–5.2 ft (1.5–1.6 m); tail length: 3–5 in (7–12 cm); height at shoulder: 27.5–43 in (70–110 cm)

**Weight** Male 126–310 lb (57–140 kg); female 125–175 lb (57–80 kg)

**Key features** Brown body; white muzzle, underparts, and rump patch; brown horns—large and curled in rams, smaller and straighter in ewes

**Habits** Active by day; sociable: congregates in same-sex groups

**Breeding** Usually single lamb born after gestation period of about 175 days. Weaned around 4–5 months; females sexually mature at 4–5 years, males at 6–7 years. May live 24 years in captivity, 12 in the wild.

**Voice** Bleating in lambs; short, deep "baa" in adults

**Diet** Mainly grasses; also forbs and some shrubs

**Habitat** Semiopen rocky terrain; alpine to dry desert

**Distribution** Southwestern Canada to western U.S. and northern Mexico

**Status** Population: 65,000–68,000; IUCN Lower Risk: conservation dependent; CITES II. Hunting now controlled, but poaching continues in some areas

# Muskox

**Common name** Muskox

**Scientific name** *Ovibos moschatus*

**Family** Bovidae

**Order** Artiodactyla

**Size** Length head/body: male 7–9 ft (2.1–2.7 m); female 6–8 ft (1.9–2.4 m); tail length: 3–5 in (7–12 cm); height at shoulder: 47–59 in (120–150 cm)

**Weight** Male 410–900 lb (186–408 kg); female 353–420 lb (160–190 kg)

**Key features** Stocky ox with short legs and neck; slight hump at shoulders; large, rounded hooves; coat black with light saddle and front; fur dense and long; sharp, curved horns in both sexes

**Habits** Normally active by day; also after dark on long winter nights; social: often forms herds

**Breeding** Single calf (twins rare) born late April–mid-June every 2 years after gestation period of 8–9 months. Weaned at 9–12 months; females sexually mature at 2 years, males at 5 years. May live at least 24 years in the wild, probably similar in captivity, but rarely kept

**Voice** Bulls roar, calves bleat

**Diet** Grasses, lichens, sedges, herbs, and shrubs such as willow and dwarf birch

**Habitat** Arctic tundra near glaciers

**Distribution** Greenland, northern Canada; reintroduced to Alaska, introduced to Russia, Norway, and Sweden

**Status** Population: 66,000–85,000. Now recovering after populations severely reduced by hunting in 19th century

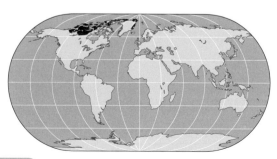

# Ibex

**Common name** Ibex

**Scientific name** *Capra ibex*

**Family** Bovidae

**Order** Artiodactyla

**Size** Length head/body: male 47–67 in (120–170 cm); female 39–51 in (100–130 cm); tail length: 5–6 in (12–15 cm); height at shoulder: 25.5–41 in (65–105 cm)

**Weight** Male 176–220 lb (80–100 kg); female 66–110 lb (30–50 kg)

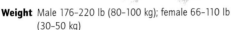

**Key features** Coat brownish-gray in alpine ibex, various colors in other subspecies; both sexes have woolly beard on chin; horns massive and thick in male, smaller in female, smooth at back, strong, transverse ridges at front

**Habits** Mainly active during day; females and young live in groups; males roam in groups or alone

**Breeding** Single young (occasionally twins) born late April–early May after gestation period of 147–161 days. Weaned at 6–7 months; females sexually mature at 2–4 years, males at 5–6 years. May live at least 22 years in captivity, 18 in the wild

**Voice** Short, whistling hiss

**Diet** Grasses, herbaceous plants, shrubs, and lichens

**Habitat** Rocky alpine crags and deserts

**Distribution** Central Europe; Afghanistan and Kashmir to Mongolia and central China; northern Ethiopia, Sudan, Egypt, Syria, and Arabia; introduced to Slovenia, Bulgaria, and U.S.

**Status** Population: unknown, but some subspecies may number only a few hundred; IUCN various subspecies listed as Critically Endangered, Endangered, and Vulnerable

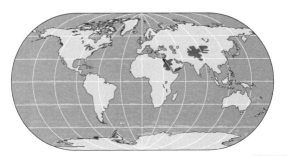

# Mountain Goat

**Common name**
Mountain goat

**Scientific name** *Oreamnos americanus*

**Family** Bovidae

**Order** Artiodactyla

**Size** Length head/body: male 4.2–5.2 ft (1.3–1.6 m); female 45–53 in (115–135 cm); tail length: 3–8 in (8–20 cm); height at shoulder: male 35–48 in (90–122 cm); female 31–36 in (80–92 cm)

**Weight** Male 101–309 lb (46–140 kg); female 101–126 lb (46–57 kg)

**Key features** Coat yellowish-white with thick, woolly underfur; long guard hairs form stiff mane on neck and rump; horns black and curved, thicker in males; short, strong legs; short tail

**Habits** Diurnal, but rests in warmest part of day; lives alone or in small groups most of year; males fight for dominance

**Breeding** Single young or twins born May–June after gestation period of about 180 days. Weaned at 3 months; sexually mature at 18 months. May live about 19 years in captivity, 14 in the wild (males); females a few more

**Voice** Various sheeplike bleating sounds

**Diet** Variety of trees, shrubs, grasses, and herbs

**Habitat** Steep cliffs, rocks, and edges of glaciers

**Distribution** Southeastern Alaska and south Yukon to Oregon, Idaho, and Montana; introduced to some other mountainous areas of North America

**Status** Population: probably about 50,000–100,000. Not threatened

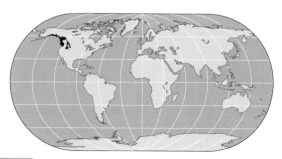

# Pronghorn

**Common name** Pronghorn (antelope)

**Scientific name** *Antilocapra americana*

**Family** Antilocapridae

**Order** Artiodactyla

**Size** Length head/body: 46–52 in (116–133 cm); tail length: 4–5.5 in (10–14 cm); height at shoulder: about 34 in (87 cm)

**Weight** Male 92.5–130 lb (42–59 kg); female 90–110 lb (41–50 kg)

**Key features** Long-legged antelope with stocky body; upperparts pale brown, white belly, flanks, throat, and rump; males have black face mask; single forward-pointing prong

**Habits** Active during day, with short feeding bouts at night; lives in single-sex herds for most of year; some populations migratory

**Breeding** Usually twins born after gestation period of 251 days. Weaned at 4–5 months; females sexually mature at 15–16 months, males at 2–3 years but breed later. May live 12 years in captivity, 9–10 in the wild

**Voice** Grunts and snorts; lambs bleat, males roar

**Diet** Forbs, shrubs, grasses; often cacti and crops

**Habitat** Rolling grassland and bush; open conifer forests

**Distribution** Western U.S., Canada, parts of northern Mexico

**Status** Population: over 1 million; IUCN various subspecies listed as Critically Endangered, Endangered, and Lower risk: conservation dependent; CITES I. Species as a whole no longer threatened

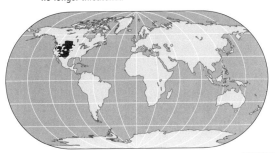

# Springhare

**Common name** Springhare (springhaas)

**Scientific name** *Pedetes capensis*

**Family** Pedetidae

**Order** Rodentia

**Size** Length head/body: 14–17 in (36–43 cm); tail length: 14.5–19 in (37–48 cm)

**Weight** 6.6–8.8 lb (3–4 kg)

**Key features** Kangaroolike rodent with very small forelimbs and long back feet; short snout; large eyes; big, leaf-shaped ears; fur thin and soft, reddish-brown to buff, paler on belly; end of tail has big black brush

**Habits** Generally nocturnal; digs burrows; lives alone but feeds in groups; hops on hind legs like a kangaroo

**Breeding** Three litters of 1 (occasionally 2) young born at any time of year after gestation period of 80 days. Weaned at 7 weeks; sexually mature at 2–3 years. May live up to 19 years in captivity, probably many fewer in the wild

**Voice** Soft grunts and high-pitched piping calls

**Diet** Roots, bulbs, and grasses; leaves and seeds of other plants, including crops; occasionally insects such as locusts and beetles

**Habitat** Desert and semidesert with dry sandy soils

**Distribution** Two populations: 1 in Kenya and Tanzania; the other in arid and semiarid parts of Angola, southern Democratic Republic of Congo, Namibia, South Africa, Botswana, Zimbabwe, and southern Mozambique

**Status** Population: unknown, probably tens of thousands; IUCN Vulnerable. Still abundant, but declining rapidly; hunted for food and as a crop pest

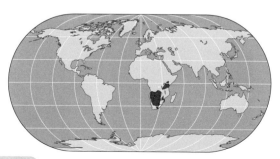

# Desert Pocket Mouse

**Common name** Desert pocket mouse (coarse-haired pocket mouse)

**Scientific name** *Chaetodipus penicillatus*

**Family** Heteromyidae

**Order** Rodentia

**Size** Length head/body: 3–5 in (8–12 cm); tail length: 3–5.5 in (8–14 cm)

**Weight** 0.5–1.5 oz (14–43 g)

**Key features** Buff-gray mouse with pale underside; fur coarse; cheek pouches open on either side of mouth

**Habits** Nocturnal; burrow-dwelling; solitary

**Breeding** Litters of 1–8 young born in spring and summer after gestation period of 23 days. Weaned at 3–4 weeks; sexually mature within a few weeks. Closely related *C. fallax* has lived 8 years in captivity; life span in the wild likely to be much shorter

**Voice** Generally silent

**Diet** Seeds and other plant material; occasionally insects, grubs, and other small invertebrates

**Habitat** Sparsely vegetated sandy desert

**Distribution** Desert regions of Utah, Nevada, California, Arizona, and New Mexico; central to northwestern Mexico

**Status** Population: unknown, but probably millions

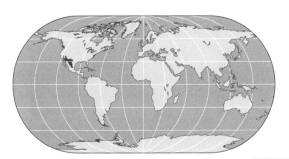

# Northern Pocket Gopher

**Common name** Northern pocket gopher (western pocket gopher)

**Scientific name** *Thomomys talpoides*

**Family** Geomyidae

**Order** Rodentia

**Size** Length head/body: 5–7 in (12–19 cm); tail length: 1.5–3 in (4–8 cm)

**Weight** 2–6 oz (57–170 g). Male up to twice as heavy as female

**Key features** Robust body with short legs and large, long-clawed feet; tail short with naked tip; very thick neck and massive head, with small eyes and ears; lips close behind prominent incisor teeth; coat short and silky, any shade of brown from near-black to creamy white

**Habits** Solitary; aggressive; burrowing; mostly nocturnal

**Breeding** Single litter of 1–10 (usually 3–5) young born in spring after gestation period of 18 days. Weaned at 40 days; sexually mature at 1 year. May live up to 4 years in the wild, probably similar in captivity, although not normally kept for very long

**Voice** Generally silent

**Diet** Roots, bulbs, tubers, stems, and leaves of various plants, including many crops

**Habitat** Prairie grassland, forest, agricultural land, and anywhere else with soil suitable for burrowing

**Distribution** Southwestern Canada and western U.S.

**Status** Population: abundant. Some subspecies may be threatened by habitat loss

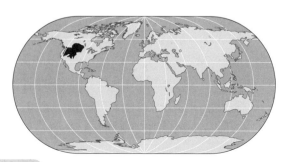

# American Beaver

**Common name**
American beaver (Canadian beaver)

**Scientific name** *Castor canadensis*

**Family** Castoridae

**Order** Rodentia

**Size** Length head/body: 31–47 in (80–120 cm); tail length: 10–20 in (25–50 cm)

**Weight** 24–66 lb (11–30 kg)

**Key features** Robust body with short legs; large, webbed hind feet; tail scaly, flattened, and paddlelike; small eyes and ears; coat dense and waterproof, light to rich dark brown

**Habits** Lives in small territorial colonies of related animals; semiaquatic; fells small trees to build lodges and dams that are of great importance to wetland ecosystem; largely nocturnal

**Breeding** Single litter of 1–9 (usually 2–4) young born in spring after gestation period of 100–110 days. Weaned at 3 months; sexually mature at 18–24 months. May live over 24 years in captivity, up to 24 in the wild

**Voice** Hisses and grunts; also announces presence by slapping tail on water surface

**Diet** Aquatic plants such as water lilies and leaves; also bark, twigs, roots, and other woody tissues of waterside trees and shrubs

**Habitat** Lakes and streams among light woodland

**Distribution** Canada, Alaska, and much of contiguous U.S.; introduced to parts of Finland

**Status** Population: 6–12 million. Abundant—recovered well after serious decline due to excessive fur trapping in 18th and 19th centuries; regulated hunting still takes place

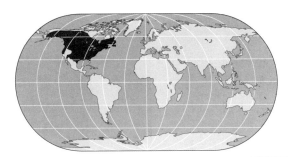

# Gray Squirrel

**Common name** Gray squirrel (American gray squirrel)

**Scientific name** *Sciurus carolinensis*

**Family** Sciuridae

**Order** Rodentia

**Size** Length head/body: 9–11 in (24–29 cm); tail length: 8–9 in (20–24 cm)

**Weight** 14–21 oz (400–600 g)

**Key features** Chunky squirrel with variable silvery to dark-gray fur, tinged with brown in summer; black individuals or subgroups also occur; tail bushy and fringed with white; ears rounded and without hairy tips

**Habits** Diurnal; tree-dwelling; also forages extensively on the ground; solitary, but nonterritorial; bold and inquisitive

**Breeding** One or 2 litters of 1–7 young born January–February and May–June after gestation period of 44–45 days. Weaned at 8 weeks; females sexually mature at 8 months, males at 10–11 months. May live up to 10 years in captivity, usually fewer in the wild

**Voice** Churring and chattering sounds; screams in distress

**Diet** Seeds and nuts, especially acorns; also buds, flowers, fruit, insects, and eggs

**Habitat** Mixed deciduous woodland

**Distribution** Southeastern Canada and eastern U.S.; introduced populations in Britain, Italy, and South Africa

**Status** Population: abundant

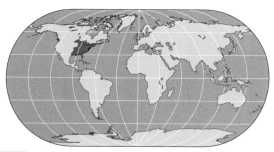

# Eurasian Red Squirrel

**Common name** Eurasian red squirrel

**Scientific name** *Sciurus vulgaris*

**Family** Sciuridae

**Order** Rodentia

**Size** Length head/body: 7–9.5 in (18–24 cm); tail length: 5.5–8 in (14–20 cm)

**Weight** 7–17 oz (200–480 g)

**Key features** Dainty squirrel with rich reddish-brown fur, white chest, and bushy tail; ears have long tufts in winter

**Habits** Diurnal; arboreal; generally solitary; does not hibernate

**Breeding** One or 2 litters of 1–8 (usually 3) young born in spring or summer after gestation period of 6 weeks. Weaned at 7–10 weeks; sexually mature at 10–12 months. May live 10 years in captivity, up to 7 in the wild

**Voice** Chattering and chucking sounds

**Diet** Pine cones, nuts, acorns, fruit, bark, and sap

**Habitat** Woodland, especially conifer

**Distribution** Most of Europe except southern England and northern and eastern Italy, where introduced gray squirrel thrives; Asia east to northeastern China

**Status** Population: abundant; IUCN Lower Risk: near threatened. Locally threatened in areas where gray squirrels have been introduced

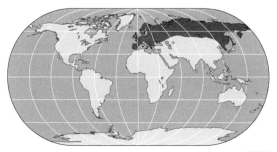

# Eastern Chipmunk

**Common name** Eastern chipmunk

**Scientific name** *Tamias striatus*

**Family** Sciuridae

**Order** Rodentia

**Size** Length head/body: 5.5-7 in (14-17 cm); tail length: 3-5 in (8-12 cm)

**Weight** 3-5 oz (85-140 g)

**Key features** Large chipmunk with reddish-brown coat, fading to cream on belly, with 5 black stripes along back separated alternately by brown-and-white fur; large internal cheek pouches; bottlebrush tail covered in short hair; ears rounded, eyes large and bright; face also has striped markings

**Habits** Diurnal; solitary; territorial; digs extensive burrows—may stay there in winter, but does not hibernate

**Breeding** One or 2 litters of 1-9 (usually 3-5) young born in spring and summer after gestation period of 31 days. Weaned at 6 weeks; sexually mature at 10-12 months. May live up to 8 years in captivity, 3 in the wild

**Voice** High-pitched chirping calls

**Diet** Nuts, seeds, acorns, fungi, fruit, and crop plants; occasionally insects, birds' eggs, and baby mice

**Habitat** Lightly wooded land with warm, dry soils and rocky crevices in which to hide

**Distribution** Eastern U.S. and southeastern Canada

**Status** Population: abundant. Threatened by persecution and habitat loss in some agricultural areas

# Woodchuck

**Common name**
Woodchuck
(groundhog, whistlepig)

**Scientific name** *Marmota monax*

**Family** Sciuridae

**Order** Rodentia

**Size** Length head/body: 16–26 in (41–66 cm); tail length: 4–10 in (10–25 cm)

**Weight** 4.5–13 lb (2–6 kg)

**Key features** Chunky, short-legged, short-tailed rodent; dense, woolly reddish-brown fur with white-tipped guard hairs; head darker, with small eyes and small, rounded ears; short, hairy tail

**Habits** Diurnal; terrestrial; burrowing; hibernates in winter

**Breeding** Single litter of 1–9 (usually 4 or 5) born in spring after gestation period of 30–32 days. Weaned at 6 weeks; sexually mature at 2 years. May live up to 15 years in captivity, 6 in the wild

**Voice** Loud whistling alarm call; also chattering, squealing, and barking noises; grinds teeth when agitated

**Diet** Fresh grasses and leaves of other plants; also seeds and fruit

**Habitat** Prairie, grasslands, and road edges

**Distribution** North America: Alaska to Idaho in the west, Newfoundland to Alabama and Arkansas in the east

**Status** Population: abundant. Has expanded range and population in some areas developed for agriculture, but hunting for fur and persecution as a pest have led to significant declines in others

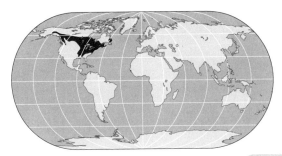

# European Marmot

**Common name**
European marmot
(alpine marmot)

**Scientific name**
*Marmota marmota*

**Family** Sciuridae

**Order** Rodentia

**Size** Length head/body:
18.5–20 in (47–52 cm); tail length: 6–8 in (15–20 cm)

**Weight** 6–10 lb (3–4.5 kg)

**Key features** Chunky body with short, muscular legs and short
tail; fur is golden-brown to gray

**Habits** Diurnal; social; burrowing; hibernates for 6–7 months
of the year

**Breeding** Single litter of 2–6 young born May–June after
gestation period of 34 days. Weaned at 40 days;
sexually mature at 18 months. May live up to 15 years
in the wild, not often kept in captivity

**Voice** Shrill whistle when alarmed; growls and screeches
when angry

**Diet** Grasses, herbs, roots, fruit, and flowers

**Habitat** Alpine meadows and rocky slopes above
1,970 ft (600 m)

**Distribution** Alpine regions of Italy, France, and Switzerland;
reintroduced to Carpathian Mountains (Poland-Slovakia
border); introduced to Germany (Black Forest) and
France (Massif Central and Pyrenees, Vosges, and
Jura Mountains)

**Status** Population: abundant. Has declined in recent centuries,
but successfully reintroduced to areas of former
(prehistoric) range

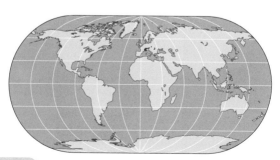

# Thirteen-Lined Ground Squirrel

**Common name** Thirteen-lined ground squirrel (thirteen-lined suslik)

**Scientific name** *Spermophilus tridecemlineatus* (*Citellus tridecemlineatus*)

**Family** Sciuridae

**Order** Rodentia

**Size** Length head/body: 4–7 in (11–18 cm); tail length: 2.5–5 in (6–13 cm)

**Weight** 4–5 oz (110–140 g)

**Key features** Compact body with short legs and furry tail up to about half length of body; coat strikingly marked with 13 alternating dark and pale stripes; the dark stripes are patterned with white spots

**Habits** Diurnal; burrowing; hibernates for up to 8 months a year

**Breeding** One (occasionally 2) litters of 2–13 young born in summer after gestation period of 28 days. Weaned at 6 weeks; sexually mature at 9–10 months. Females may live up to 11 years in captivity, similar in the wild; males about half as long

**Voice** Twittering chirps and chattering sounds; growls and piercing whistle used as alarm call

**Diet** Grasses, seeds, insects (especially beetles, grasshoppers, and caterpillars); also eggs, baby mice, and birds

**Habitat** Grass prairie and farmland

**Distribution** Southern Canada (Alberta) south to Ohio and southern Texas

**Status** Population: abundant

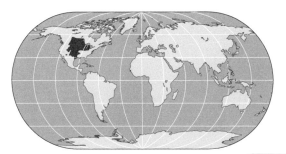

# Black-Tailed Prairie Dog

**Common name**
Black-tailed prairie dog
(plains prairie dog)

**Scientific name** *Cynomys ludovicianus*

**Family** Sciuridae

**Order** Rodentia

**Size** Length head/body: 10–12 in (26–31 cm); tail length: 3–4 in (7–9.5 cm). Female about 10% smaller than male

**Weight** 20–53 oz (575–1,500 g)

**Key features** Sturdily built squirrel with short legs and short tail with black tip; coat buffy gray

**Habits** Diurnal and fossorial; highly social but also territorial; does not hibernate

**Breeding** Single litter of 1–8 (usually 3–5) young born in spring after gestation period of 34–37 days. Weaned at 5–7 weeks; sexually mature at 2 years. May live up to 8 years in captivity, 5 in the wild

**Voice** Various barks, squeaks, and soft churring sounds

**Diet** Grasses and herbs

**Habitat** Open short-grass plains and prairies; also pastureland

**Distribution** Great Plains of North America from southern Canada (Saskatchewan) to northern Mexico

**Status** Population: more than 1 million; IUCN Lower Risk: near threatened. Has declined due to habitat modification and persecution

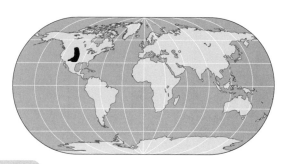

# Southern Flying Squirrel

**Common name** Southern flying squirrel
(eastern flying squirrel)

**Scientific name** *Glaucomys volans*

**Family** Sciuridae

**Order** Rodentia

**Size** Length head/body: 8–9 in
(21–24 cm); tail length: 3–4 in (8–10 cm)

**Weight** 1.7–4 oz (50–120 g)

**Key features** Small silvery-gray squirrel with bushy but flattened
tail and furry gliding membrane stretching from wrists to
ankles; head large with big ears and huge black eyes

**Habits** Nocturnal, social, and gregarious; arboreal; hoards food—
does not hibernate; "flies" by gliding on flaps of skin
stretched between front and back limbs

**Breeding** One or 2 litters of 1–6 (usually 2–4) young born in
spring and summer after gestation period of 40 days.
Weaned at 8–9 weeks; sexually mature at 9 months.
May live up to 14 years in captivity, fewer in the wild

**Voice** Chirping and squeaking calls, many of which are too
high-pitched for humans to hear

**Diet** Nuts, acorns, bark, fungi, fruit, and lichen; occasionally
eats insects and meat

**Habitat** Woodland

**Distribution** Southeastern Canada, eastern U.S., and Central
America south to Honduras

**Status** Population: abundant. Has declined in some areas due
to deforestation, but generally secure; may be
responsible for the decline of the related but much rarer
northern flying squirrel in some areas

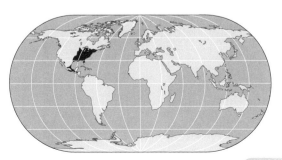

# House Mouse

**Common name**
House mouse

**Scientific name**
*Mus musculus*

**Family** Muridae

**Order** Rodentia

**Size** Length head/body: 3–4.5 in (8–11 cm); tail length: 3–4 in (8–10 cm)

**Weight** 0.5–1 oz (14–28 g)

**Key features** Small, slim body; pointed face with large, sparsely haired ears; long, scaly pink tail; fur grayish-brown, often greasy and smelly

**Habits** Generally nocturnal; often aggressive; excellent climber, also swims well; lives wild and in association with people

**Breeding** Up to 14 litters of 4–10 young born at any time of year after gestation period of 19–21 days (more if female is suckling previous litter). Weaned at 3 weeks; sexually mature at 6 weeks. May live up to 6 years in captivity, 2 in the wild

**Voice** Squeaks

**Diet** Omnivorous: almost anything of plant or animal origin, including leather, wax, cloth, soap, and paper; also chews man-made materials such as plastics and synthetic fabrics

**Habitat** Farms, food supplies, fields, and houses

**Distribution** Almost worldwide

**Status** Population: billions. Less common than previously in many developed countries due to intensive pest control and mouse-proof buildings

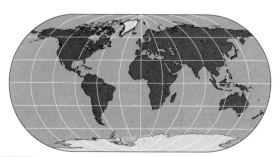

# Brown Rat

**Common name** Brown rat (common rat, Norway rat)

**Scientific name** *Rattus norvegicus*

**Family** Muridae

**Order** Rodentia

**Size** Length head/body: 9–11 in (22–29 cm); tail length: 7–9 in (17–23 cm)

**Weight** 9–28 oz (255–790 g)

**Key features** Typical rat with short legs, longish fingers and toes, and pointed face; ears pink and prominent; scaly tail noticeably shorter than head and body; fur dull grayish-brown, fading to white or pale gray on belly

**Habits** Generally nocturnal; social; cautious at first but can become bold; climbs and swims well

**Breeding** Up to 12 litters of 1–22 (usually 8 or 9) young born at any time of year (but mostly in spring and summer) after gestation period of 21–26 days. Weaned at 3 weeks; sexually mature at 2–3 months. May live up to 6 years in captivity, 3 in the wild

**Voice** Loud squeaks when frightened or angry

**Diet** Anything edible, including fruit, grain, meat, eggs, wax, and soap; will catch and kill other small animals

**Habitat** Almost anywhere food can be found

**Distribution** Worldwide in association with humans; not normally in more sparsely populated areas of the world

**Status** Population: several billion

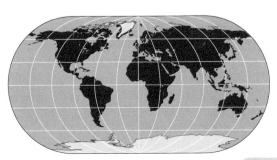

# Ship Rat

**Common name** Ship rat (black rat, house rat, roof rat, plague rat)

**Scientific name** *Rattus rattus*

**Family** Muridae

**Order** Rodentia

**Size** Length head/body: 6–9.5 in (15–24 cm); tail length: 4.5–12 in (12–30 cm)

**Weight** 5–10 oz (150–280 g)

**Key features** Slender body with long, scaly tail; face pointed; hairless ears larger than those of brown rat; fur black or gray-brown

**Habits** Nocturnal; social; excellent climber; a pest of stored foodstuffs; often associated with human habitation, especially around ports and on ships

**Breeding** Up to 5 litters of 1–16 (usually 7 or 8) young born at any time of year after gestation period of 21–29 days. Weaned at 3 weeks; sexually mature at 2–4 months. May live up to 4 years in captivity, 2 in the wild

**Voice** Loud squeaks and whistles

**Diet** Varied; all kinds of foods stored by humans, especially fond of fruit

**Habitat** Varied; forests and farmland, but does well in towns

**Distribution** Originally from India; now found along tropical and temperate coasts of all continents except Antarctica

**Status** Population: many millions. Increasingly rare due to intensive persecution, but unlikely to receive protection because of bad reputation

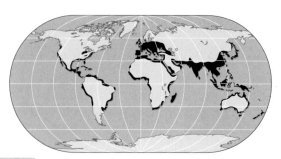

# Wood Mouse

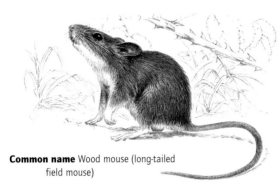

**Common name** Wood mouse (long-tailed field mouse)

**Scientific name** *Apodemus sylvaticus*

**Family** Muridae

**Order** Rodentia

**Size** Length head/body: 3.5–4 in (9–10 cm); tail length: 3–4.5 in (7–11.5 cm)

**Weight** 0.5–1 oz (14–28 g)

**Key features** Small, neat-looking mouse with rounded body, large ears, large black eyes, and very long tail; fur golden-brown; white on belly

**Habits** Nocturnal or crepuscular; more social in winter than summer; climbs and jumps well; burrows and stores food

**Breeding** Up to 4 litters of 2–9 (usually 4–7) young born spring to fall (season varies with climatic region) after gestation period of 19–20 days. Weaned at 18–20 days; sexually mature at 2 months. May live 3–4 years in captivity, rarely more than 20 months in the wild

**Voice** Squeaks

**Diet** Omnivorous: seeds, buds, shoots, fruit, fungi, and nuts; also snails, insects (especially grubs and caterpillars), and other arthropods; cereals such as corn and oats

**Habitat** Woodland, farmland, scrubland, and gardens; also mountains and sand dunes

**Distribution** Iceland, British Isles, most of mainland Europe (except northern Scandinavia) east to Central Asia and south to Persian Gulf; also northwestern Africa

**Status** Population: abundant

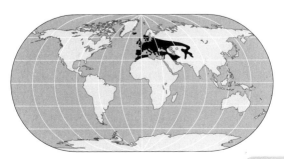

# Western Harvest Mouse

**Common name** Western harvest mouse

**Scientific name** *Reithrodontomys megalotis*

**Family** Muridae

**Order** Rodentia

**Size** Length head/body: 2.5–3 in (6–8 cm); tail length: 2–3 in (5–8 cm)

**Weight** 0.3–0.5 oz (8–14 g)

**Key features** Tiny mouse with brown fur; white underside; tail long, thin, and sparsely furred; ears large; incisor teeth have prominent grooves

**Habits** Nocturnal; can be solitary or social; excellent climber; does not hibernate

**Breeding** Several litters of 1–9 (usually 3–5) young born March–November, occasionally also in winter, after gestation period of 21 days. Weaned at 21 days; sexually mature at 17 weeks. May live up to 30 months in captivity, 18 in the wild

**Voice** High-pitched "buzzing" calls

**Diet** Seeds and green shoots, especially grasses

**Habitat** Short prairie grass, sagebrush desert, pasture, light woodland, and salt marsh

**Distribution** Southern Alberta and British Columbia; central and western U.S. south to Indiana and central Mexico

**Status** Population: abundant. Agricultural deforestation has allowed species range to expand since European settlement of North America

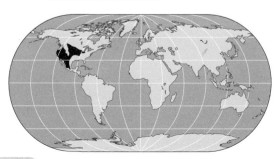

# Deer Mouse

**Common name**
Deer mouse (white-footed mouse)

**Scientific name** *Peromyscus maniculatus*

**Family** Muridae

**Order** Rodentia

**Size** Length head/body: 2.5–4 in (7–10 cm);
tail length: 2–5 in (5–12 cm)

**Weight** 0.4–1 oz (11–28 g)

**Key features** Russet-bodied, with white underside and legs; tail
2-tone and variable in length; head large with huge,
sparsely furred, round ears; black eyes and long whiskers

**Habits** Mostly nocturnal; stores food for winter; does not enter
full hibernation

**Breeding** Three to 4 litters of 1–9 young born in spring and
summer in north of range (anytime in south) after
gestation period of 22–30 days. Weaned at 3–4 weeks;
females sexually mature at 6 weeks, males rarely breed
before 6 months. May live up to 8 years in captivity,
rarely more than 2 in the wild

**Voice** Squeaks and buzzing sounds; drums forefeet on ground
when excited

**Diet** Omnivorous: seeds and grains, fruit, flowers, and other
plant material; also insects and other invertebrates

**Habitat** Varied; includes scrubland, prairie, desert, alpine areas,
boreal forest, and woodland

**Distribution** All of North America except tundra regions of
Canada and southeastern U.S; also Mexico

**Status** Population: very abundant

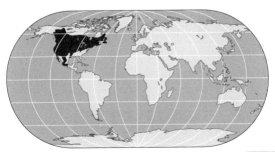

# Desert Wood Rat

**Common name**
Desert wood rat (pack rat, trade rat)

**Scientific name** *Neotoma lepida*

**Family** Muridae

**Order** Rodentia

**Size** Length head/body: 6–9 in
(15–23 cm); tail length: 0.5 in (1 cm)

**Weight** 0.4–1 lb (0.2–0.5 kg)

**Key features** Brownish-gray rat with pale underside and feet;
ears round; furry tail up to half length of body

**Habits** Nocturnal, solitary, and timid; constructs large "houses"
above ground, collecting building material from wide
area; does not hibernate

**Breeding** Two or 3 litters of 1–5 young born at any time of year
after gestation period of 30–40 days. Weaned at 4
weeks; sexually mature at 2 months. May live up to 7
years in captivity, several years in the wild

**Voice** Generally silent

**Diet** Leaves, seeds, roots, and fleshy cactus pads; also insects
and other small invertebrates

**Habitat** Desert

**Distribution** Deserts of southwestern U.S. and northwestern
Mexico, including Baja California

**Status** Population: abundant

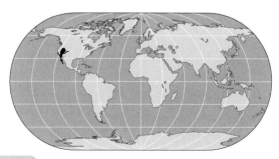

# Golden Hamster

**Common name** Golden hamster (Syrian hamster)

**Scientific name** *Mesocricetus auratus*

**Family** Muridae

**Order** Rodentia

**Size** Length head/body: 6.5–7 in (17–18 cm); tail length: 0.5 in (1 cm)

**Weight** 3.5–4 oz (99–113 g)

**Key features** Short-tailed animal with sandy fur fading to white on belly; head broad with prominent rounded ears and huge cheek pouches; females have 12–16 mammae

**Habits** Mostly nocturnal; burrowing; socially aggressive; capable of hibernation

**Breeding** Three to 5 litters of 2–16 young born at any time of year (mostly spring and summer) after gestation period of 16–19 days. Weaned at 20 days; sexually mature at 8 weeks. May live 3 years in captivity, fewer in the wild

**Voice** Generally silent

**Diet** Very varied: includes seeds, shoots, fruit, and other plant material; also insects and other invertebrates and meat scavenged as carrion

**Habitat** Steppe and dry, rocky, scrubland

**Distribution** Aleppo region of northwestern Syria

**Status** Population: probably a few hundred in the wild; IUCN Endangered. Many thousands bred in captivity every year

# Mongolian Gerbil

**Common name** Mongolian gerbil (Mongolian jird)

**Scientific name** *Meriones unguiculatus*

**Family** Muridae

**Order** Rodentia

**Size** Length head/body:
4–7 in (10–18 cm);
tail length: 4–7 in (10–18 cm)

**Weight** 1.4–2.5 oz (40–71 g)

**Key features** Small, sand-colored rodent; long, furry tail with brushy tip; hind feet long, all toes bear long claws; ears small but prominent

**Habits** Lives alone or in family groups; active day and night and all year round; sleeps and stores food in burrows

**Breeding** Up to 3 litters of 1–12 (usually 4–7) young born in spring, summer, or fall after gestation period of 19–21 days. Weaned at 3 weeks; sexually mature at 15 weeks. May live several years in captivity, rarely more than 2 in the wild

**Voice** Various squeaking sounds; also signals by drumming feet on ground

**Diet** All kinds of plant material, including seeds, shoots, roots, and fruit; also insects

**Habitat** Desert

**Distribution** Mongolia, southern Siberia, and northern Chinese provinces of Sinkiang and Manchuria

**Status** Population: abundant

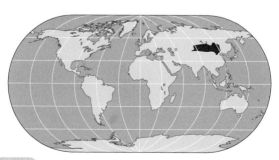

# Norway Lemming

**Common name**
Norway lemming

**Scientific name** *Lemmus lemmus*

**Family** Muridae

**Order** Rodentia

**Size** Length head/body: 3–6 in (7–15.5 cm); tail length: about 0.5–1 in (1–2 cm)

**Weight** 0.4–5 oz (11–142 g)

**Key features** Rounded body and head; very short tail; thick coat creamy-yellow on underside, legs, and feet, but deep reddish-brown on back; darker on shoulders, head, and face; ears small and hidden in fur; eyes small and bright; thumb of each front foot bears large, flat snow claw

**Habits** Active at any time of day; does not hibernate; lives in burrows in ground or snow; swims well; aggressive and unsociable; overcrowded populations occasionally undertake mass migrations

**Breeding** Up to 6 litters of 1–13 (usually 5–8) young born in spring and summer (or every 21 days all year round under ideal conditions) after gestation period of 16–23 days. Weaned at 14–16 days; females sexually mature at 2–3 weeks, males at 3–4 weeks. May live up to 2 years, usually fewer, in the wild; not normally kept in captivity

**Voice** Various squeaks and whistles

**Diet** Mostly mosses; also leaves and shoots of grasses and sedges, lichen, fruit, and bark

**Habitat** Tundra

**Distribution** Norway, Sweden, Finland, and extreme northwestern Russia

**Status** Population: generally abundant but fluctuates wildly from year to year

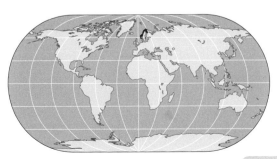

# Field Vole

**Common name** Field vole (short-tailed vole)

**Scientific name** *Microtus agrestis*

**Family** Muridae

**Order** Rodentia

**Size** Length head/body: 3–5 in (8–13 cm); tail length: 1–2 in (2–5 cm)

**Weight** 0.5–1.8 oz (14–50 g)

**Key features** Round bodied and short nosed, with short pinkish tail; fur uniformly gray-brown above, paler on belly; ears short, often hidden by fur

**Habits** Mostly nocturnal and crepuscular; territorial and aggressive; digs burrows; also creates runways in grass

**Breeding** Up to 7 litters of 1–12 young (usually 4–6) born spring to fall after gestation period of 19–25 days. Weaned at 2 weeks; females sexually mature at 4 weeks, males at 6 weeks. May live up to 2 years in captivity, usually fewer in the wild

**Voice** Loud squeaks; chirps and chattering noises when angry

**Diet** Herbivorous: mostly grass; also leaves, shoots, and bark of other plants

**Habitat** Grassland: common in lightly grazed pasture and field edges with longish grass; also heaths and moorland

**Distribution** Throughout northern Europe, including Scandinavia and Britain (but not Ireland); east to central Siberia

**Status** Population: abundant, probably hundreds of millions

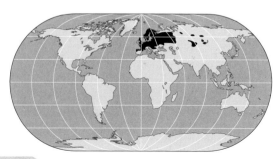

# Southern Red-Backed Vole

**Common name**
Southern red-backed vole

**Scientific name** *Clethrionomys gapperi*

**Family** Muridae

**Order** Rodentia

**Size** Length head/body: 3–5 in
(8–13 cm); tail length: 1–2 in (3–5 cm)

**Weight** 0.2–1.5 oz (6–43 g)

**Key features** Rounded body with short legs; tail about half
length of body; fur grayish-brown with reddish flush
along back; face short with prominent black eyes and
large, rounded ears

**Habits** Active day and night and all year round; territorial;
climbs well

**Breeding** Up to 4 litters of 1–11 young born early spring to fall
after gestation period of 17–20 days. Weaned at 3
weeks; sexually mature at 3 months. May live over 4
years in captivity, up to 20 months in the wild

**Voice** Soft, chirping alarm call and audible clattering of teeth

**Diet** Fruit, nuts, fungi, lichen, green shoots, and other
vegetation; also insects

**Habitat** Tundra, moorland, mossy forest undergrowth, and
woodland floors

**Distribution** Southern Canada from British Columbia to
Newfoundland; northern coterminous U.S. south
to Arizona

**Status** Population: abundant

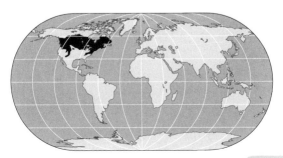

# Muskrat

**Common name** Muskrat

**Scientific name** *Ondatra zibethicus*

**Family** Muridae

**Order** Rodentia

**Size** Length head/body: 9–13 in (23–33 cm); tail length: 7–11.5 in (18–29 cm)

**Weight** 1.5–4 lb (0.6–1.8 kg)

**Key features** Huge brown or black rat with glossy fur and large, partially webbed hind feet; tail naked and slightly flattened from side to side

**Habits** Mostly nocturnal and crepuscular; social but bad tempered; semiaquatic

**Breeding** Up to 6 litters of 1–11 young born at any time of year (spring and summer in north of range) after gestation period of 25–30 days. Weaned at 2–3 weeks; sexually mature at 6–8 weeks in south of range, later in north. May live up to 10 years in captivity, rarely more than 3 in the wild

**Voice** Growls when annoyed

**Diet** Mostly aquatic plants such as reeds, rushes, cattails, and water lilies; also grasses and animal matter, including fish and shellfish

**Habitat** Pools, lakes, rivers, marshes, and swamps with plenty of plant life

**Distribution** Southern Canada and most of U.S.; patchy in California and Texas; introduced in Eurasia and South America

**Status** Population: abundant—many thousands, perhaps millions. Trapped for fur and meat; considered a pest in parts of introduced range in Europe

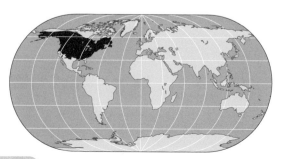

# Water Vole

**Common name** Water vole (north European water vole, water rat)

**Scientific name** *Arvicola terrestris*

**Family** Muridae

**Order** Rodentia

**Size** Length head/body: 5–9 in (12–23 cm); tail length: 1.5–5.5 in (4–14 cm). Northern animals larger than those in south

**Weight** 3–11 oz (85–312 g)

**Key features** Chubby, ratlike rodent with rounded head and body, blunt face, and thin, hairy tail; rich glossy brown fur that grows quite long

**Habits** Semiaquatic; solitary; active day and night all year round

**Breeding** Two to 5 litters of 2–8 (usually 4–6 young) born between spring and fall after gestation period of 20–22 days. Weaned at 2–3 weeks; sexually mature at 1–12 months (British voles only breed after their first winter). May live up to 5 years in captivity, rarely more than 18 months in the wild

**Voice** Usually silent; may give harsh clicking call when alarmed; squeaks when angry

**Diet** Grasses, sedges, roots; occasionally catches and eats fish

**Habitat** Banks of slow-flowing streams and rivers; also away from water in meadows and pastures

**Distribution** Widespread throughout most of Europe east through Siberia to Mongolia; absent from Iceland, Ireland, much of France, Spain, and Portugal; patchy distribution in Greece

**Status** Population: abundant, many thousands. Dramatic recent decline of British population threatens species with extinction there

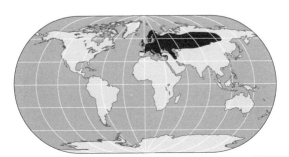

# Lesser Blind Mole Rat

**Common name** Lesser blind mole rat (Balkan blind mole rat)

**Scientific name** *Nannospalax leucodon* (formerly *Spalax leucodon*)

**Family** Muridae

**Order** Rodentia

**Size** Length head/body: 6–11 in (15–27 cm)

**Weight** 3.5–7.5 oz (100–213 g)

**Key features** Long body with short legs and large, clawed feet; no visible tail, eyes, or ears; face dominated by large nose and huge protruding incisor teeth; light-brown fur with prominent white facial stripe

**Habits** Active day and night; burrowing: hardly ever emerges at surface; solitary and territorial

**Breeding** Litters of 1–5 (usually 2–4) young born January–April after gestation period of 1 month. Weaned at 3–4 weeks; probably sexually mature at about 2–3 months. May live up to 4.5 years, usually many fewer in the wild, not normally kept in captivity

**Voice** Generally silent, but appears to signal by drumming head on roof of tunnels

**Diet** Roots and tubers, including crops such as potatoes; also acorns and plant stems

**Habitat** Well-drained soils under wooded or open ground

**Distribution** Balkan peninsula, Romania, and Bulgaria

**Status** Population: not known, probably several thousand; IUCN Vulnerable. Increasingly rare and patchy in distribution

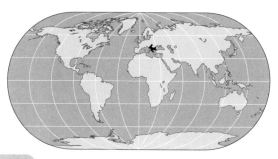

# Hazel Dormouse

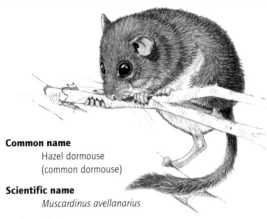

**Common name**
Hazel dormouse
(common dormouse)

**Scientific name**
*Muscardinus avellanarius*

**Family** Gliridae

**Order** Rodentia

**Size** Length head/body: 2.5–3.5 in
(6–9 cm); tail length: 2–3 in
(5.5–7.5 cm)

**Weight** 0.5–1.4 oz (14–40 g)

**Key features** Small dormouse with bright-yellow fur and long,
furry tail; face short; eyes large and black; ears small
but prominent

**Habits** Nocturnal; social; arboreal; hibernates for 6 months
of the year

**Breeding** One or 2 litters of 2–7 (usually 3–5) young born in
midsummer after gestation period of 22–24 days.
Weaned at 40 days; sexually mature at about 11
months. May live up to 6 years in captivity, at least 5
in the wild

**Voice** Generally silent, but may utter small, chirping contact
sounds; wheezes when disturbed asleep

**Diet** Nuts, seeds, flowers and buds, fruit, and insects;
occasionally eggs and baby birds

**Habitat** Deciduous woodland with dense understory of nut-
bearing trees such as hazel; also mature hedgerows

**Distribution** Western and central mainland Europe, except
northern Scandinavia, Iberian Peninsula, and Turkey

**Status** Population: probably about 2 million; IUCN Lower Risk:
near threatened

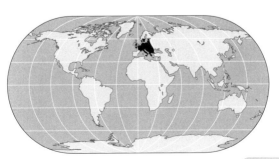

# African Porcupine

**Common name** African porcupine (crested porcupine, North African porcupine)

**Scientific name** *Hystrix cristata*

**Family** Hystricidae

**Order** Rodentia

**Size** Length head/body: 23.5– 39.5 in (60–100 cm); tail length: 3–6.5 in (8–17 cm)

**Weight** 26.5–60 lb (12–27 kg)

**Key features** Large rodent; dark-brown to black fur; long black-and-white spines on back and rump; crest of stiff hairs from head to mid-back; legs sturdy, feet have powerful claws; blunt snout, medium-sized ears, small eyes

**Habits** Nocturnal; lives in burrows in groups but forages alone

**Breeding** One or 2 litters of 1–4 (usually 1 or 2) young born at any time of year after gestation period of 3.5 months. Weaned at 6–7 weeks; sexually mature at about 1 year. May live up to 20 years in captivity, about 14 in the wild

**Voice** Grunts, growls, and "peeps"; also shakes hollow quills on rump to make rattling sound when threatened

**Diet** Roots, tubers, fruit, and tree bark; carrion and bones; crops such as yams and corn

**Habitat** Savanna, woodland, and rocky steppe, especially on hilly ground

**Distribution** Throughout northern Africa (except Sahara Desert) south to Democratic Republic of Congo and Tanzania; also Italy, including Sicily

**Status** Population: abundant. Persecuted as an agricultural pest in many areas

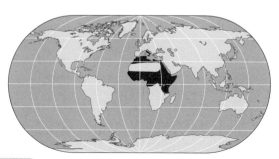

# North American Porcupine

**Common name** North American porcupine (quillpig)

**Scientific name** *Erethizon dorsatum*

**Family** Erethizontidae

**Order** Rodentia

**Size** Length head/body: 25–34 in (64.5–86 cm); tail length: 5.5–12 in (14–30 cm)

**Weight** 7.7–40 lb (3.5–18 kg)

**Key features** Large rodent covered in stiff, brown to black fur; long, yellow spines on head, back, rump, flanks, and tail; feet have long, thick claws; short face with small, dark eyes and small ears hidden in hair

**Habits** Usually nocturnal; partially arboreal; lives alone or in small groups when breeding or sheltering in winter

**Breeding** Single young born April–June after 7.5 months' gestation. Weaned at 2–6 weeks; sexually mature at 2 years. May live 18 years in captivity, similar in the wild

**Voice** Grunts, growls, coughs, barks, and whines; also makes clattering sound with teeth

**Diet** Plant material, including leaves, shoots, buds, flowers, fruit, seeds, nuts, twigs, bark, wood; also gnaws bones

**Habitat** Mixed forest; also tundra, farmland, scrubland, and desert close to wooded areas

**Distribution** North America from Alaska throughout most of Canada and the continental U.S. south to northern Mexico and the Carolinas

**Status** Population: abundant

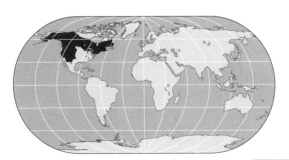

# Chinchilla

**Common name** Chinchilla

**Scientific name** *Chinchilla lanigera*

**Family** Chinchillidae

**Order** Rodentia

**Size** Length head/body: 9–15 in (23–38 cm); tail length: 3–6 in (7.5–15 cm)

**Weight** 14–28 oz (400–800 g)

**Key features** Rabbitlike rodent; short legs, small 4-toed feet; bushy tail; very soft, dense, silvery-gray fur; head large; big round black eyes; large oval ears; long dark whiskers

**Habits** Usually active between dusk and dawn; may bask in sunshine during day; colonial; nimble and fast moving

**Breeding** One to 2 litters of 1–6 (usually 2–3) young born May–November after gestation period of 111 days. Weaned at 6–8 weeks; sexually mature at 8 months. May live up to 20 years in captivity, rarely more than 10 in the wild

**Voice** Growls and squeaks; also makes chattering noises with teeth

**Diet** Broad range of plant material

**Habitat** Rocky mountain slopes

**Distribution** Andes Mountains of southern Peru, Bolivia, northern Chile, and northern Argentina

**Status** Population: fewer than 10,000 in the wild; IUCN Vulnerable; CITES I. Hunting for the fur industry has decimated numbers; does well in captivity, but extremely rare in the wild

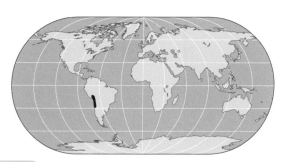

# Guinea Pig

**Common name** Guinea pig (domestic cavy)

**Scientific name** *Cavia porcellus*

**Family** Caviidae

**Order** Rodentia

**Size** Length head/body: 8–16 in (20–40 cm)

**Weight** 1.1–3.3 lb (0.5–1.5 kg)

**Key features** Robust, ratlike body with short legs, no tail, and large head; small ears and round eyes; coat usually grayish-brown in feral forms, variable in domestic varieties

**Habits** Nocturnal; social; timid; terrestrial; can swim well when necessary

**Breeding** Several litters of 1–13 young born at any time of year after gestation period of 63–68 days. Weaned at 3 weeks; sexually mature at 2 months. May live up to 8 years in captivity, probably fewer in the wild

**Voice** Conversational squeaks, chirps, and chattering

**Diet** All kinds of plant matter

**Habitat** Usually captive; feral animals live in grassland and forest margins

**Distribution** Captive and feral only; farmed in Andean region of South America

**Status** Population: abundant. Does not exist in original wild state

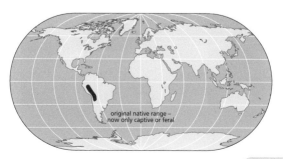

original native range – now only captive or feral

# Common Agouti

**Common name** Common agouti (spotted agouti)

**Scientific name** *Dasyprocta punctata*

**Family** Dasyproctidae

**Order** Rodentia

**Size** Length head/body: 16–24.5 in (41–62 cm); tail length: 0.5–2 in (1–5 cm)

**Weight** 3–9 lb (1.3–4 kg)

**Key features** Slender, piglike rodent with coarse, but glossy brown fur, paler on underside; face long and rabbitlike with large eyes and broad ears; legs short and slim, with 4 developed toes on front feet and 3 on back, all with large hooflike claws; tail insignificant

**Habits** Active by day; terrestrial; burrowing; pairs mate for life and are aggressively territorial; can run fast

**Breeding** One or 2 litters of 1–4 (usually 1 or 2) young born at any time of year after gestation period of 3–4 months. Weaned at 20 weeks; sexually mature at about 1 year. May live up to 17 years in captivity, fewer in the wild

**Voice** Growls and yapping barks; high-pitched scream when alarmed

**Diet** Plant material, especially fruit, tubers, succulent leaves, and tender new shoots

**Habitat** Forest, scrub, grassland, and farmland

**Distribution** Central and South America from southern Mexico to northern Argentina; introduced to several Caribbean islands

**Status** Population: abundant. Has declined in many areas due to hunting

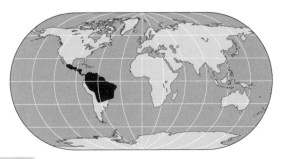

# Coypu

**Common name** Coypu
(nutria, swamp beaver)

**Scientific name** *Myocastor coypus*

**Family** Myocastoridae

**Order** Rodentia

**Size** Length head/body: 17–25 in
(43–63 cm); tail length:
10–16.5 in (25–42 cm)

**Weight** 11–37.5 lb (5–17 kg)

**Key features** Large, ratlike animal with coarse, reddish-brown
coat and soft, velvety underfur; tail long, scaly, and
sparsely furred; head large with prominent orange
incisor teeth and small eyes and ears; hind feet webbed

**Habits** Active day and night; semiaquatic, excellent swimmer
and diver; lives in waterside burrows in pairs or small
family groups

**Breeding** Two to 3 litters of 1–13 (usually 4–6) young born in
spring and summer after gestation period of 4.5 months.
Weaned at 1–8 weeks; sexually mature at 3–7 months.
May live up to 7 years in captivity, rarely more than 4 in
the wild

**Voice** Grunts and growls; also squawks and grinds teeth

**Diet** Aquatic plants and nearby crops

**Habitat** Marshes, lakes, slow-flowing rivers, and streams

**Distribution** Native range covers southern South America,
including southern Brazil, Paraguay, Bolivia, and
Uruguay; introduced elsewhere

**Status** Population: abundant. Widely trapped for fur; now a
serious nuisance outside native range

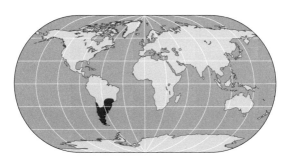

# Capybara

**Common name** Capybara

**Scientific name** *Hydrochaeris hydrochaeris*

**Family** Hydrochaeridae

**Order** Rodentia

**Size** Length head/body: 42–53 in (106–135 cm)

**Weight** 77–145 lb (35–66 kg)

**Key features** Tall, barrel-bodied rodent with slender legs and sparse reddish-brown hair; no tail; front feet have 4 toes, hind feet 3; large head with rectangular profile and deep muzzle; small ears and eyes; male has lozenge-shaped gland on top of face

**Habits** Semiaquatic; social; colonial; usually active by day, but often nocturnal where disturbed

**Breeding** One (occasionally 2) litters of 1–8 (usually 3–5) young born at any time of year after gestation period of 150 days. Weaned almost immediately; sexually mature at 12 months. May live up to 12 years in captivity, 9 or 10 in the wild

**Voice** Whistles, grunts, purring and clicking sounds; also coughing barks

**Diet** Grasses and aquatic plants

**Habitat** Grassland and forest alongside rivers and pools

**Distribution** South America: south of Panama and east of Andes Mountains, including Colombia, Venezuela, Brazil, and Paraguay south as far as northeastern Argentina

**Status** Population: numerous, but total unknown; IUCN Lower Risk: conservation dependent. Declining in many areas

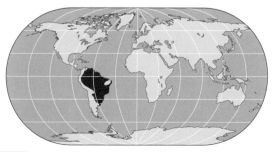

# Naked Mole Rat

**Common name** Naked mole rat (sand puppy)

**Scientific name** *Heterocephalus glaber*

**Family** Bathyergidae

**Order** Rodentia

**Size** Length head/body: 3–3.5 in (8–9 cm); tail length: 1–2 in (3–5 cm)

**Weight** 1–2.8 oz (28–80 g)

**Key features** Small, naked rodent with short legs and tail; a few whiskers on face and body; prominent incisor teeth; tiny eyes and ears with no external ear flaps; large feet have 5 clawed toes

**Habits** Adapted to a life underground; colonial and highly social, with division of labor and suppression of breeding in subordinates; active mostly by day

**Breeding** Litters of 1–27 young born at any time of year after gestation period of 67 days. Weaned at 1 month; sexually mature at 7 months, but few animals have opportunity to breed. May live up to 25 years in captivity, probably similar in the wild

**Voice** Generally silent

**Diet** Plant roots and tubers

**Habitat** Lives underground in dry soils of desert and semidesert

**Distribution** East Africa, including Ethiopia, Somalia, and Kenya

**Status** Population: not known

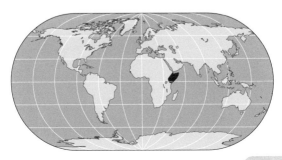

# European Rabbit

**Common name** European rabbit (Old World rabbit, domestic rabbit)

**Scientific name** *Oryctolagus cuniculus*

**Family** Leporidae

**Order** Lagomorpha

**Size** Length head/body: 14–20 in (35–50 cm); tail length: 1.5–3 in (4–8 cm)

**Weight** 3–6.6 lb (1.3–3 kg)

**Key features** Stoutly built animal with powerful legs usually disguised by crouching stance; tail short and fluffy; head rounded with large, round eyes and long, erect oval ears; fur dense and soft, usually grayish-brown to black, paler on underside

**Habits** Mostly nocturnal but also active by day; lives in colonies in clustered burrows

**Breeding** Up to 7 litters of 1–9 (usually 5 or 6) young born in spring or summer after gestation period of 28–33 days. Weaned at 21 days; sexually mature at 3 months. May live up to 15 years in captivity, rarely more than 10 in the wild; most live fewer than a few months

**Voice** Usually silent; sharp squeals in pain or fright; drums feet to signal alarm

**Diet** Grass; also stems and leaves of other plants; nibbles bark in winter

**Habitat** Grassland

**Distribution** Much expanded by introductions over past 1,000 years; now occurs throughout Europe and northern Africa, also established in Australia and New Zealand

**Status** Population: extremely abundant, hundreds of millions. Widely persecuted as a pest

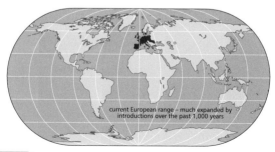

current European range – much expanded by introductions over the past 1,000 years

# Snowshoe Hare

**Common name** Snowshoe hare (snowshoe rabbit, bush rabbit)

**Scientific name** *Lepus americanus*

**Family** Leporidae

**Order** Lagomorpha

**Size** Length head/body: 16–22 in (41–55 cm); tail length: 1.5–2 in (4–5 cm)

**Weight** 3–4 lb (1.4–1.8 kg)

**Key features** Small, rabbitlike hare with reddish-gray fur, northern specimens turn white in winter; feet large and furry with long toes

**Habits** Solitary but not antisocial; mainly nocturnal; active all year; nonburrower; has runways above ground; secretive and nervous; runs fast, leaps high, and swims well

**Breeding** Up to 4 litters of 1–8 young born spring and summer after gestation period of 36 days. Weaned at 3 weeks, sexually mature at 9–12 months. May live up to 7 years in captivity, 5 in the wild

**Voice** Generally silent, may hiss and grunt in aggression and squeal when captured

**Diet** Grass and other green herbage, buds, twigs, and bark of young trees

**Habitat** Coniferous and evergreen boreal forest

**Distribution** Canada, Alaska, and northern U.S.; lives farther south in mountainous regions

**Status** Population: abundant, fluctuates on 10-year cycle. Local declines due to habitat loss; introduced to areas such as Newfoundland at the expense of local species

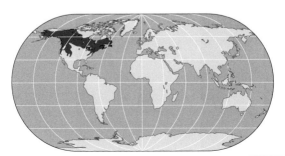

# Black-Tailed Jackrabbit

**Common name** Black-tailed jackrabbit

**Scientific name** *Lepus californicus*

**Family** Leporidae

**Order** Lagomorpha

**Size** Length head/body: 18.5–25 in (47–63 cm); tail length: up to 4 in (10 cm)

**Weight** 3.3–4.4 lb (1.5–4 g)

**Key features** Large hare with huge, erect black-tipped ears; legs long and slender; face has flat profile and large bulging eyes; fur grizzled gray-brown, paler below; dark dorsal stripe blends into black tail

**Habits** Active mainly in the evening; social; terrestrial, fast-moving, and nimble

**Breeding** Two to 6 litters of 1–6 (usually 3 or 4) young born at any time of year after gestation period of 41–47 days. Weaned at about 3 weeks; sexually mature at 7–8 months, but will often not breed until following year. May live up to 6 years in captivity, 5 in the wild

**Voice** Generally silent

**Diet** Grass and other plants of arid zones, including sagebrush, cactus, juniper, and mesquite; may raid cereal crops and orchards

**Habitat** Desert, prairie, and pasture in arid and semiarid areas

**Distribution** Southwestern United States and Mexico

**Status** Population: abundant, but fluctuates on 10-year cycle. Has increased in range and population since European settlement thanks to predator control

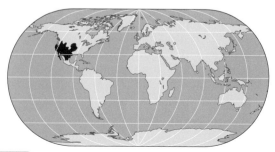

# Arctic Hare

**Common name** Arctic hare (polar hare, Greenland hare)

**Scientific name** *Lepus arcticus*

**Family** Leporidae

**Order** Lagomorpha

**Size** Length head/body: 20-21 in (51-53 cm); tail length: 1.5-4 in (4.5-10 cm)

**Weight** 5.5-15 lb (2.5-7 kg)

**Key features** Gray or brown in summer with white tail; white all over in winter, except for tips of ears, which are black

**Habits** Usually solitary, but sometimes forms large groups; normally lives out in the open or among boulders

**Breeding** One litter of 2-8 young (average 5) born June or July after gestation period of 53 days. Weaned at about 8 or 9 weeks; sexually mature by following summer. May live about 7 years in the wild, not normally kept in captivity

**Voice** Normally silent

**Diet** Woody plants, moss, lichens, roots and flowers of willows; also some grasses

**Habitat** Tundra

**Distribution** Far north of Canada and Greenland south to Hudson Bay and Newfoundland

**Status** Population: total figure unknown. Common

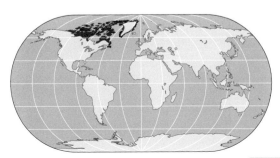

# Brown Hare

**Common name**
Brown hare

**Scientific name**
*Lepus europaeus*

**Family** Leporidae

**Order** Lagomorpha

**Size** Length head/body: 19–27 in
(48–68 cm); tail length: 3–5 in (8–13 cm)

**Weight** 5.5–15 lb (2.5–7 kg)

**Key features** Resembles large rabbit, but
with longer, black-tipped ears. Fur warm
brown and grizzled, with bright orange
flanks; staring yellow eyes

**Habits** Mainly nocturnal, but also active by day; generally
solitary, but may gather to feed; temporary pairs form in
spring; wide-ranging, nonterritorial; conspicuously active
in spring, with much chasing and "boxing"

**Breeding** Three litters of (usually 4) young born
February–October after gestation period of 41–42 days.
Weaned at about 4 weeks; sexually mature at 6–8
months. May live up to 13 years in the wild, does not
normally thrive in captivity

**Voice** Normally silent, but screams in distress

**Diet** Mainly grasses, also small herbaceous plants;
bark and shoots of bushes; frequently raids crops,
especially cereals

**Habitat** Open grassland, farmland, and steppe; grassy mountain
slopes up to 5,000 ft (1,500 m)

**Distribution** Western Europe to Siberian lowlands south to Iran;
introduced to Ireland, South America, Australia, New
Zealand, and other places

**Status** Population: total figures unknown, but likely to be
several million. Widespread and generally common, but
locally declining

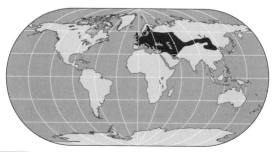

# Eastern Cottontail

**Common name** Eastern cottontail

**Scientific name** *Sylvilagus floridanus*

**Family** Leporidae

**Order** Lagomorpha

**Size** Length head/body: 11–13 in (29–34 cm); tail length: 0.5–1 in (1–3 cm)

**Weight** 2–4 lb (0.9–1.8 kg)

**Key features** Large rabbit with dense, soft, woolly gray-brown fur and white powder-puff tail; head small and rounded with long, oval ears

**Habits** Solitary and often bad tempered; active mostly at night

**Breeding** Three to 4 litters of 2–12 (usually 3–6) young born spring to early fall after gestation period of 26–32 days. Weaned at 16–22 days; sexually mature at 2–3 months. May live up to 10 years in captivity, up to 5 in the wild, but rarely more than 3

**Voice** Generally silent; may squeal in distress or alarm; females sometimes grunt in warning

**Diet** Grasses and herbaceous plants in summer; twigs, buds, and bark in winter

**Habitat** Varied; forests, swamps, meadows, and scrubland

**Distribution** Eastern North America from southern Manitoba, Ontario, and Quebec in Canada through eastern and midwestern U.S. and Central America to Colombia and Venezuela

**Status** Population: abundant

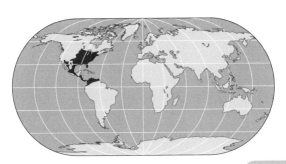

# American Pika

**Common name** American pika (common pika, Rocky Mountain pika, calling hare, mouse hare, coney)

**Scientific name** *Ochotona princeps*

**Family** Ochotonidae

**Order** Lagomorpha

**Size** Length head/body: 6.5–8.5 in (16–22 cm)

**Weight** 4–6.5 oz (110–180 g)

**Key features** Compact, rounded body with short neck and short legs; no visible tail; blunt head has short, round ears; fur is grayish-brown to buff with buffy underparts

**Habits** Solitary; aggressively territorial; terrestrial; diurnal; does not hibernate, but stores food for winter

**Breeding** Two litters of 1–6 (usually 3) young born spring and summer after gestation period of 30 days. Weaned at 30 days; sexually mature at 3 months. May live up to 7 years in captivity, rarely more than 5 in the wild

**Voice** Sharp alarm whistle and shrill courtship "song"; juveniles squeak

**Diet** Green plant material supplemented with stockpiled hay during winter

**Habitat** Boulder-strewn mountain slopes (talus) with patches of alpine grassland

**Distribution** Mountainous parts of western Canada and U.S. from British Columbia to central California and Colorado

**Status** Population: abundant

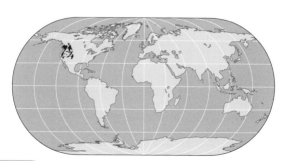

# Western European Hedgehog

**Common name** Western European hedgehog (European hedgehog, urchin)

**Scientific name** *Erinaceus europaeus*

**Family** Erinaceidae

**Order** Insectivora

**Size** Length head/body: 6–10 in (16–26 cm); tail length: 0.5–1 in (1.5–3 cm)

**Weight** To 1–2.2 lb (0.5–0.9 kg), usually 17–28 oz (480–800 g)

**Key features** Spiny animal that rolls into a ball when alarmed; short tail; 5 long claws on each foot; general color grizzled brown and cream

**Habits** Nocturnal; normally lives alone; does not defend territory

**Breeding** Usually 4–6 (up to 8) young born in early summer after gestation period of 32–34 days (late litters born August–September). Weaned at 4–6 weeks; sexually mature at 1 year. May live up to 7 years in the wild, perhaps 10; fewer in captivity

**Voice** Snorts and grunts; piglike squeal if attacked

**Diet** Almost anything edible found at ground level, including beetles, worms, caterpillars, eggs, slugs, and occasional soft fruit

**Habitat** Farmland, short grass areas, hedges, woodlands, town parks, and gardens

**Distribution** Western Europe from Britain and southern Scandinavia to the Mediterranean east to Romania

**Status** Population: several million. Widespread and fairly abundant, especially in suburban areas

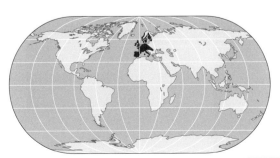

# Common Tenrec

**Common name** Common tenrec (greater tenrec, tailless tenrec)

**Scientific name**
    *Tenrec ecaudatus*

**Family** Tenrecidae

**Order** Insectivora

**Size** Length: 10–15 in (26–39 cm); tail length: 0.4–0.6 in (1–1.5 cm)

**Weight** 3.5–5.3 lb (1.6–2.4 kg)

**Key features** Buff, grayish, or reddish-brown animal with hairs and spines; crest of long, rigid spines at nape of neck; long snout and extremely wide gape; short legs and tail

**Habits** Generally solitary; peaks of activity in the early and late parts of the night; shelters during the day in a burrow, hollow log, or under rocks; hibernates underground

**Breeding** Litters of up to 32 (usually about 15) young born December–January after gestation period of 56–64 days. Weaned at 6–8 weeks; sexually mature at 6 months. May live over 6 years in captivity, probably fewer in the wild

**Voice** Squeaks and squeals; low hissing noise when aggravated

**Diet** Mainly invertebrates, plus fruit, vegetation, and occasional small reptiles, amphibians, and mammals

**Habitat** Areas with brush or other cover near water, from sea level to about 2,900 ft (900 m)

**Distribution** Madagascar; introduced to Mauritius, Réunion Island, and the Comoro and Seychelles archipelagos

**Status** Population: unknown, but probably many thousands (including introduced populations)

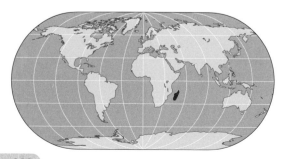

# Eurasian Common Shrew

**Common name** Eurasian common shrew

**Scientific name** *Sorex araneus*

**Family** Soricidae

**Order** Insectivora

**Size** Length head/body: 2–3 in (5–7 cm); tail length: about 1 in (2.5 cm)

**Weight** 0.2–0.5 oz (5–15 g)

**Key features** Small mammal; brown all over, paler below; long, pointed nose, small ears and tiny eyes; tail about half the length of head and body

**Habits** Active day and night; rushes around constantly; solitary and aggressively territorial; lives in shallow burrows and tunnels in soil and leaf litter

**Breeding** About 6 (but as many as 10) young born April–September in up to 4 litters per season after gestation period of 22–25 days. Weaned at 3–4 weeks. May live a maximum of 23 months in captivity, similar in the wild, but average life span less than 1 year, and half die within 2 months

**Voice** Loud piercing shrieks or squeaks when angry or alarmed

**Diet** Mostly insect larvae and soil invertebrates; small worms

**Habitat** Woodland, farmland, hedgerow, and tundra; especially abundant in damp places

**Distribution** Most of Europe from Mediterranean to Arctic and from Britain to western China

**Status** Population: many millions. Very common animal

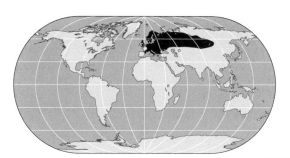

# American Water Shrew

**Common name**
American water shrew

**Scientific name**
*Sorex palustris*

**Family** Soricidae

**Order** Insectivora

**Size** Length head/body: 3–4 in (7.5–10.5 cm); tail length: 2.5–3 in (6–7.5 cm)

**Weight** 0.3–0.5 oz (8.5–14 g)

**Key features** Quite large; blackish-gray coat sometimes becomes browner in summer; pale to dark-gray underside; 2-colored tail; distinctive fringe of stiff white hairs on sides of feet; tiny eyes and ears; red tips to teeth

**Habits** Solitary; active day and night but mostly just after sunset and before dawn; hunts in water

**Breeding** Litters of 3–10 young born late February–June after gestation period of about 21 days. Weaned at 28 days; sexually mature at 2 months in early-born young, 10 months in late-born young. May live about 18 months in captivity, similar in the wild

**Voice** High-pitched squeaks during territorial disputes

**Diet** Aquatic invertebrates such as caddisfly larvae and insect nymphs; occasionally small fish; on land takes flies, earthworms, and snails

**Habitat** Waterside habitats, especially in northern forests; prefers humid conditions

**Distribution** Canada; southeastern Alaska; mountain regions of U.S. into Utah and New Mexico, Sierra Nevada to California

**Status** Population: unknown, but likely to be millions. Widespread and abundant

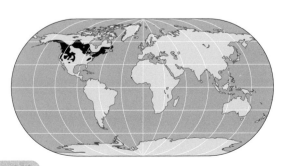

# Grant's Golden Mole

**Common name** Grant's golden mole (desert golden mole)

**Scientific name** *Eremitalpa granti*

**Family** Chrysochloridae

**Order** Insectivora

**Size** Length head/body: 3–3.5 in (8–9 cm)

**Weight** About 0.5–1 oz (14–28 g)

**Key features** Smallest of the golden moles, with pale silvery fur

**Habits** Makes shallow burrows in sand; probably mainly forages on the surface at night

**Breeding** Probably gives birth in October or November; average litter size likely to be small, since the few pregnant females found so far contained only a single embryo each. Rate of development not known. Life span also unknown, but probably about 3 years

**Voice** Normally silent

**Diet** Insects; spiders; also small reptiles dug from shallow burrows in the sand or among grass roots

**Habitat** Coastal sand dunes

**Distribution** Narrow fringe of southwestern Africa, including Cape Province and Little Namaqualand (South Africa) and part of Namibia

**Status** Population: unknown. Rare

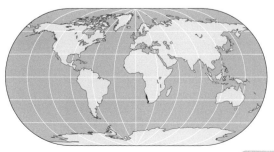

# Common Tree Shrew

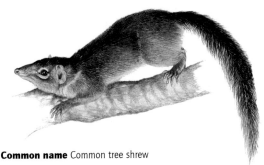

**Common name** Common tree shrew

**Scientific name** *Tupaia glis*

**Family** Tupaiidae

**Order** Scandentia

**Size** Length head/body:
5.5–6 in (14–15 cm); tail length: 6–6.5 in (15–16.5 cm)

**Weight** 3.5–7 oz (100–200 g)

**Key features** Small, squirrel-like animal with a sharply pointed nose; coat color olive to dark brown on back and flanks, creamy white to orange-red below; tail covered in long hairs like a squirrel; emits a distinctly musky smell

**Habits** Active during the day; forages on the ground or in low bushes; nests in tree roots and among fallen timber

**Breeding** Twins born after gestation period of 40–52 days. Weaned at 5 weeks; sexually mature at 4 months. May live 12.5 years in captivity, unlikely to survive as long in the wild

**Voice** Squeals, squeaks, hisses, and chattering alarm calls

**Diet** Insects, fruit, seeds, and leaves

**Habitat** Tropical rain forest

**Distribution** Southern Malay Peninsula, Sumatra, and surrounding islands

**Status** Population: unknown, but likely to be many thousands. Habitats threatened by deforestation, so numbers likely to be declining

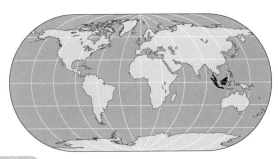

# Golden-Rumped Elephant Shrew

**Common name** Golden-rumped elephant shrew

**Scientific name** *Rhynchocyon chrysopygus*

**Family** Macroscelididae

**Order** Macroscelidea

**Size** Length head/body: 9–12 in (23.5–31.5 cm); tail length: 7–10 in (19–26.5 cm)

**Weight** 14.4–15.5 oz (408–440 g)

**Key features** Size of a large rat, with elongated snout; coat dark reddish-black with yellow patch on rump; black ears, feet, and legs; fur fine, stiff, and glossy; male canine teeth are longer than those of female

**Habits** Active during day, foraging in leaf litter; spends nights in leaf nests on forest floor; forms monogamous pairs, but they usually sleep and forage separately

**Breeding** Single young born after gestation period of 42 days. Weaned at 2 weeks; sexually mature at perhaps 3–6 months. May live up to 4 years in captivity, similar in the wild

**Voice** Range of squeaks and squeals

**Diet** Wide variety of invertebrates, including grasshoppers, crickets, beetles, spiders, centipedes, worms, and termites

**Habitat** Open coastal forest

**Distribution** Kenya

**Status** Population: may now be fewer than 5,000, perhaps a fraction of that; IUCN Endangered. Threatened by habitat loss

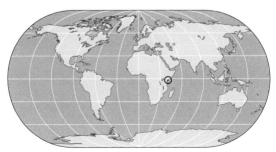

# Giant Anteater

**Common name** Giant anteater

**Scientific name** *Myrmecophaga tridactyla*

**Family** Myrmecophagidae

**Order** Xenarthra

**Size** Length head/body: 39–51 in (100–130 cm); tail length: 25.5–35.5 in (65–90 cm)

**Weight** Male 53–86 lb (24–39 kg); female 48–77 lb (22–35 kg)

**Key features** Narrow, powerful body; small head with long, tapering snout; coat gray with black stripe from shoulders to chest and neck; hair coarse and stiff; long, bushy tail

**Habits** Solitary; generally diurnal; breaks into ant and termite nests

**Breeding** One young born in spring after gestation period of 190 days. Weaned at 6 months; sexually mature at 2 years. May live up to 26 years in captivity, unknown in the wild

**Voice** Generally silent

**Diet** Ants and termites; occasional beetle larvae and fruit

**Habitat** Grassland, swamp, and lowland tropical forest

**Distribution** Central America from southern Belize through South America to Northern Argentina

**Status** Population: unknown, but probably thousands; IUCN Vulnerable; CITES II

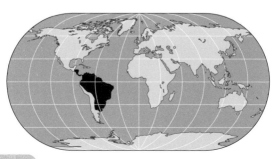

# Three-Toed Sloth

**Common name** Three-toed sloth
(brown-throated three-toed sloth)

**Scientific name** *Bradypus variegatus*

**Family** Bradypodidae

**Order** Xenarthra

**Size** Length head/body: 22–24 in
(56–61 cm); tail length: 2.5–3 in
(6–7 cm)

**Weight** 7.7–10 lb (3.5–4.5 kg)

**Key features** Long, shaggy fur; forelegs noticeably longer than
hind legs; general color grayish-fawn, often with green
tinge; small eyes; stumpy tail

**Habits** Hangs from branches, rarely descends to ground; stays
in same tree for days at a time; moves only very slowly;
active during day and at night

**Breeding** Single young born each year after gestation period of
5 months. Weaned at about 1 month, but stays with
mother for further 4–6 months; sexually mature at about
2 years. May live over 20 years in the wild, not normally
kept in captivity

**Voice** Normally silent

**Diet** Leaves collected from tree canopy

**Habitat** Lowland tropical forests

**Distribution** Honduras south to northern Argentina

**Status** Population: unknown, but probably declining. Close
relative *B. torquatus* is classified Endangered by IUCN

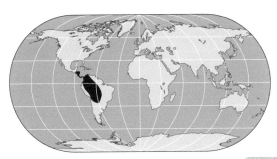

# Nine-Banded Armadillo

**Common name** Nine-banded armadillo
(long-nosed armadillo)

**Scientific name**
*Dasypus novemcinctus*

**Family** Dasypodidae

**Order** Xenarthra

**Size** Length head/body: 14.5–17 in (37–43 cm); tail length:
9.5–14.5 in (24–37 cm)

**Weight** 12–17 lb (5.5–7.5 kg). Female usually smaller than male

**Key features** Hard, shiny skin with scaly legs and tail; about
8–11 flexible bands around middle of body; long ears
and snout

**Habits** Generally nocturnal; shuffles around seeking food; lives
in shallow burrows

**Breeding** Four young born in spring after gestation period of
120 days (plus variable period of delayed implantation).
Weaned at 4–5 months; sexually mature at about 1 year.
May live at least 22 years in captivity, probably fewer in
the wild

**Voice** Constant, quiet grunting and sniffing when out foraging;
otherwise silent

**Diet** Mostly insects, especially termites; occasional worms,
snails, birds' eggs, and frogs

**Habitat** Short grass, forest floor, and farmland

**Distribution** Southern U.S. south to Uruguay and northern
Argentina and west to Peru; also Grenada and Trinidad
and Tobago in the West Indies

**Status** Population: abundant

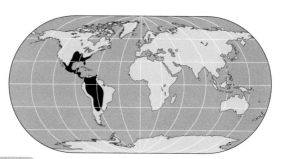

# Aardvark

**Common name** Aardvark

**Scientific name** *Orycteropus afer*

**Family** Orycteropodidae

**Order** Tubulidentata

**Size** Length head/body: 41–51 in (105–130 cm); tail length: 18–25 in (45–63 cm)

**Weight** 88–143 lb (40–65 kg)

**Key features** Muscular, piglike animal with long nose, long tail, and big ears; fur is coarse and sparse

**Habits** Solitary, shy, nocturnal, and rarely seen; digs large burrows

**Breeding** Single young born after gestation period of about 7 months. Weaned at 6 months; sexually mature at 2 years. May live up to 18 years in captivity, probably similar in the wild

**Voice** Occasional grunts

**Diet** Termites, ants, and insect larvae caught on long, sticky tongue

**Habitat** Grassland, open woodland, and scrub where ants and termites are abundant throughout year; avoids stony soils and flooded areas

**Distribution** Patchily distributed throughout most of sub-Saharan Africa

**Status** Population: unknown. Widespread, but exterminated in many areas

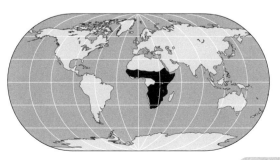

# Indian Flying Fox

**Common name** Indian flying fox

**Scientific name** *Pteropus giganteus*

**Family** Pteropodidae

**Order** Chiroptera

**Size** Length head/body: 9–12 in (23–30 cm); forearm length: 6.5–7 in (16.5–18 cm); wingspan: 47–67 in (120–170 cm)

**Weight** Male 2–3.5 lb (0.9–1.6 kg); female 1.3–2.5 lb (0.6–1.1 kg)

**Key features** Large bat with a dark-brown body and black wings; male has light-yellow color on back of neck and shoulders

**Habits** Roosts in trees in large, mixed-sex groups; feeds at night on ripe fruit

**Breeding** Single young born usually in February after gestation period of 4–5 months. Weaned at 5 months; probably sexually mature at 1–2 years. May live up to 30 years in captivity, about 15 in the wild

**Voice** Variety of squawks and loud screams

**Diet** Ripe fruit, including mangoes, bananas, papayas, figs

**Habitat** Forests and swamps, always near a large body of water

**Distribution** Maldives, Pakistan, India, Sri Lanka, and Myanmar (Burma)

**Status** Population: unknown, but probably many thousands; CITES II

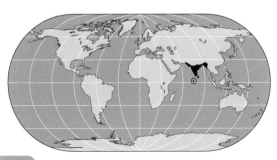

# Egyptian Rousette Bat

**Common name**
Egyptian rousette bat

**Scientific name** *Rousettus aegyptiacus*

**Family** Pteropodidae

**Order** Chiroptera

**Size** Length head/body: 4–7 in (9.5–18 cm); tail length: 0.5–1 in (1–2 cm); forearm length: 2.5–4 in (6.5–10 cm); wingspan: 16–20 in (41–51 cm)

**Weight** 3–6 oz (85–170 g)

**Key features** Smallish fruit bat; male much larger than female; gray-brown color, underparts paler; rounded ears and large eyes

**Habits** Roosts communally in caves, tombs, temples, and rock crevices; active during the day and at night; activity peaks at dawn and dusk

**Breeding** Usually single offspring or occasionally twins born October–December after gestation period of 4 months. Probably weaned at 2–3 months; sexually mature at about 1 year. May live over 20 years in captivity, probably similar in the wild

**Voice** Loud clicking echolocation call, often sufficiently low-pitched (15–150 kHz) to be audible to humans; variety of social calls, including screams and barks

**Diet** Fruit juices, flower pollen, and nectar

**Habitat** Wherever there is fruit and flowers

**Distribution** North Africa from Senegal to Egypt south to South Africa; Cyprus, Turkey, and Yemen east to Pakistan

**Status** Population: many thousands. Widespread and common

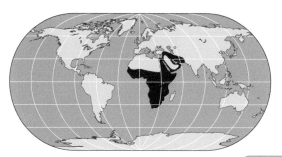

# Vampire Bat

**Common name** Vampire bat

**Scientific name** *Desmodus rotundus*

**Family** Phyllostomidae

**Order** Chiroptera

**Size** Length head/body: 3–3.5 in (7–9 cm); forearm length: 2–2.5 in (5–6.3 cm); wingspan: about 20 in (50 cm)

**Weight** 0.5–1.8 oz (15–50 g)

**Key features** Dark-gray bat, paler on underside; snout flattened; vertical groove in lower lip

**Habits** Strictly nocturnal; usually lives in colonies of 20–100; roosts in caves, hollow trees, and old mines

**Breeding** Single young born once a year after gestation period of about 7 months. Weaned at 10 months; sexually mature at 1 year. May live at least 19.5 years in captivity, 15 in the wild

**Voice** Ultrasonic squeaks (too high-pitched for humans to hear); also aggressive squeaks if other vampires attempt to feed close by

**Diet** Feeds exclusively on blood, normally taken from mammals, including humans

**Habitat** Dry and wet areas of tropical and subtropical Central and South America

**Distribution** From Argentina and central Chile to northern Mexico; also Trinidad

**Status** Population unknown, but many thousands. Abundant, but probably declining

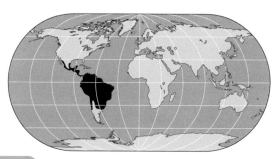

# False Vampire Bat

**Common name** False vampire bat (greater false vampire, Indian false vampire)

**Scientific name** *Megaderma lyra*

**Family** Megadermatidae

**Order** Chiroptera

**Size** Length head/body: 3–4 in (7.5–10 cm); forearm length: 2.5–3 in (6.5–7 cm); wingspan: about 30 in (70 cm)

**Weight** 1.4–2.1 oz (40–60 g)

**Key features** Large ears joined over forehead, each with divided tragus; large, erect nose-leaf forming spike on snout; fur grayish-brown above, whitish-gray below

**Habits** Nocturnal; flies low around trees and bushes to hunt small animals; roosts in groups of fewer than 30

**Breeding** Normally only 1 offspring born per year after gestation period of 150–160 days. Weaned at 2–3 months; males sexually mature at 15 months, females at 19 months. Not normally kept in captivity, probably lives at least 10 years in the wild

**Voice** Social and faint echolocation calls

**Diet** Carnivorous: preys on rodents, birds, frogs, lizards, invertebrates, and other bats

**Habitat** Variety of habitats with broad-leaved trees; roosts in caves, well shafts, crevices, large buildings, as well as tree holes

**Distribution** Afghanistan to southern China south to Sri Lanka and Malay Peninsula

**Status** Population: total figure unknown; likely to be thousands

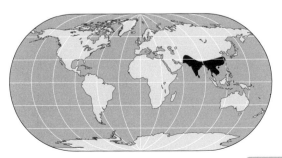

# Mexican Free-Tailed Bat

**Common name** Mexican or Brazilian free-tailed bat (guano bat)

**Scientific name** *Tadarida brasiliensis*

**Family** Molossidae

**Order** Chiroptera

**Size** Length head/body: 3.5–4 in (9–10 cm); tail length: 1–1.5 in (2.5–4 cm); forearm length: 1.5–2 in (4–5 cm); wingspan: 12–14 in (30–35 cm)

**Weight** 0.4–0.5 oz (11–14 g)

**Key features** Medium-sized bat with tail that projects well over tail membrane; ears broad; velvety reddish to black fur; wings long and narrow

**Habits** Roosts in groups of up to 20 million individuals; flies high, hunting insects at night

**Breeding** Single baby born in June after gestation period of about 90 days. Weaned at 6 weeks; sexually mature at about 1 year. May live at least 18 years in the wild

**Voice** Ultrasonic echolocation calls at 40–62 kHz; variety of social calls, including squeals, chirps, and buzzing audible to humans

**Diet** Small insects such as mosquitoes, flies, beetles, moths

**Habitat** Wide variety of habitats from desert to pine and broad-leaved forest; roosts in caves, old mines, hollow trees, and buildings

**Distribution** U.S. to Chile, Argentina, and southern Brazil; Greater and Lesser Antilles

**Status** Population: many millions; IUCN Lower Risk: near threatened. Believed to be fewer now than in recent past

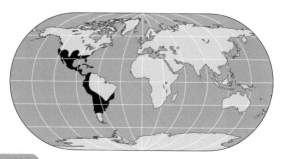

# Little Brown Bat

**Common name**
Little brown bat

**Scientific name** *Myotis lucifugus*

**Family** Vespertilionidae

**Order** Chiroptera

**Size** Length head/body: 3-4 in
(8-10 cm); forearm length: about
1.5 in (3.5-4 cm); wingspan: 9-11 in (22-27 cm)

**Weight** 0.25-0.45 oz (7-13 g)

**Key features** Small, fluttery bat with glossy fur of shades of
brown; underside paler; small, black ears with short,
rounded tragus; long hairs on toes

**Habits** Hunts insects over water; females gather in summer
nursery roosts, often in buildings; sexes hibernate
together in caves over winter

**Breeding** Single young born May–July after gestation period of
60 days. Weaned at 3 weeks; sexually mature in first
year in southern parts of range, second year farther
north. May live several years in captivity, 30 in the wild

**Voice** Short pulse echolocation calls 38–78 kHz, peaking at
about 40 kHz, too high-pitched for humans to hear

**Diet** Insects caught on wing, especially mosquitoes,
caddisflies, mayflies, and midges

**Habitat** Urban and forested areas; summer roosts in buildings or
under bridges, usually near water; hibernation roosts in
caves or mines

**Distribution** Alaska to Labrador and Newfoundland (Canada)
south to Distrito Federal (Mexico)

**Status** Population: probably several million. Not
seriously threatened

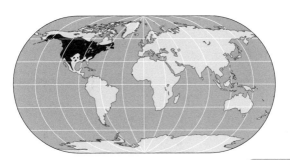

# Lesser Horseshoe Bat

**Common name**
Lesser horseshoe bat

**Scientific name**
*Rhinolophus hipposideros*

**Family** Rhinolophidae

**Order** Chiroptera

**Size** Length head/body: 1.5-2 in (4-4.5 cm); tail length: 1-1.5 in (2-3 cm); forearm length: about 0.4 cm (about 0.2 in); wingspan: 7.5-10 in (19-25 cm)

**Weight** 0.2-0.3 oz (5-9 g)

**Key features** Small, delicate bat with fine, fluffy gray fur; horseshoe-shaped nose-leaf

**Habits** Nocturnal; flies fast with shallow wing beats; hibernates alone, but summer roosts often colonial

**Breeding** Single baby born mostly mid-June–early July after gestation period of about 4 months. Weaned at 6-7 weeks; sexually mature at 1 year. May live at least 21 years in the wild, soon dies in captivity

**Voice** Quiet chirping noises using very high frequencies of 108-110 kHz

**Diet** Small moths, mosquitoes, flies, and beetles; mostly taken on the wing but some from the ground

**Habitat** Prefers wooded areas on limestone; hibernates in caves; often uses warm roof spaces as nursery roosts in northern parts

**Distribution** Southern Europe from Ireland east to Kyrgyzstan and Kashmir

**Status** Population: unknown; IUCN Vulnerable. Threatened with extinction in northern Europe

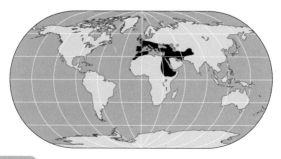

# Fisherman Bat

**Common name**
Fisherman bat (bulldog bat)

**Scientific name** *Noctilio leporinus*

**Family** Noctilionidae

**Order** Chiroptera

**Size** Length head/body: 4–5 in (10–13 cm); forearm length: 3–4 in (8–10 cm); wingspan: 11–20 in (28–51 cm)

**Weight** 2.1–3.1 oz (60–88 g)

**Key features** Large bat with heavy doglike muzzle; nostrils slightly tubular and downward pointing with "hare-lip" fold of skin hanging below; large ears; tragus with serrated edge; upperparts bright reddish-orange in males, gray or dull brown in females

**Habits** Hunts surface-swimming fish and insects at night over water; roosts in groups of 30 to several hundred; active year-round

**Breeding** Single young born after 4 months' gestation. Weaned at 3–4 months; sexually mature at about 1 year. May live 11.5 years in captivity, probably more in the wild

**Voice** High-pitched chirping echolocation calls; lower-frequency communication calls, including warning honk

**Diet** Mainly fish, but also crustaceans and insects

**Habitat** Near rivers, lakes, lagoons, or other water; roosts in caves, rock clefts, and fissures

**Distribution** Southern Mexico to Guianas, Peru, southern Brazil, northern Argentina, Trinidad, Greater and Lesser Antilles, and southern Bahamas

**Status** Population: probably low thousands

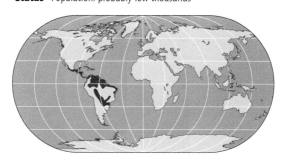

# Long-Eared Bat

**Common name**
Long-eared bat (whispering bat)

**Scientific name** *Plecotus auritus*

**Family** Vespertilionidae

**Order** Chiroptera

**Size** Length head/body: 1.5–2 in (4–5 cm); tail length: 1.5–2 in (4–5 cm); forearm length: 1–1.5 in (3–4 cm); wingspan: 9–11 in (24–28 cm)

**Weight** 0.2–0.4 oz (6–12 g)

**Key features** Medium-sized bat; ears as long as body; fur brown, long, soft, and wispy

**Habits** Active at night; one of most frequent species in house roofs, bedrooms, and bat boxes (artificial roosts); hibernates in cracks in walls of caves, mines, cellars, and old buildings

**Breeding** Single young (twins rare) born from mid-June after gestation period of about 3 months. Weaned at 4–6 weeks; sexually mature in second year. May live 22 years in the wild, does not survive long in captivity

**Voice** Occasional squeak; very quiet echolocation calls

**Diet** Moths, spiders, and caterpillars

**Habitat** Woodlands, parks, and gardens; often associated with houses, especially in north

**Distribution** Most of western Europe; scattered localities across Central Asia to China; Sakhalin Island (Russia) and Japan

**Status** Population: unknown, but probably about 1–2 million. One of the most common European bats

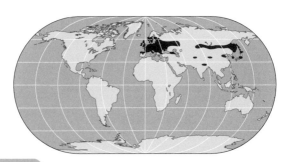

# Virginia Opossum

**Common name** Virginia opossum
(common opossum, possum)

**Scientific name** *Didelphis virginiana*

**Family** Didelphidae

**Order** Didelphimorphia

**Size** Length head/body: 14–22 in (35–55 cm); tail length: 10–21 in (25–54 cm)

**Weight** 4.5–12 lb (2–5.5 kg)

**Key features** Cat-sized animal with short legs and long, naked tail; pointed snout, large black eyes, and round, naked ears; white-tipped guard hairs make coat appear shaggy; hind feet have opposable first toe; female has up to 15 teats in well-developed pouch

**Habits** Mostly active at night; solitary; swims and climbs well

**Breeding** Up to 56 (usually about 21) young born after 13 days' gestation. Young emerge from pouch at 70 days. Weaned at 3–4 months; sexually mature at 6–8 months. May live up to 5 years in captivity, 3 in the wild

**Voice** Clicking sounds; also growls, hisses, and screeches when angry

**Diet** Small animals, including reptiles, mammals, and birds; invertebrates such as insects; plant material, including fruit and leaves; carrion; human refuse

**Habitat** Wooded areas or scrub, usually near water-courses or close to swamps

**Distribution** Eastern and central U.S.; West Coast south through Central America to Nicaragua

**Status** Population: abundant. Widespread; increasing in numbers and range

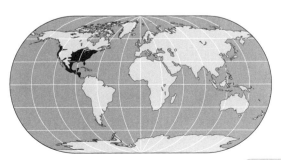

# Tasmanian Devil

**Common name** Tasmanian devil

**Scientific name** *Sarcophilus harrisii*

**Family** Dasyuridae

**Order** Dasyuromorphia

**Size** Length head/body: 21–31 in (53–80 cm); tail length: 9–12 in (23–30 cm); height at shoulder: up to 12 in (30 cm). Male bigger than female

**Weight** 9–26 lb (4–12 kg)

**Key features** Small, squat animal like a small bear; heavy-looking, muscular head; barrel body; short, furry tail; fur mostly dark-brown, lighter on muzzle; white chest band and patches on rump or flanks; female has 4 teats in a small, rear-opening pouch

**Habits** Nocturnal; usually solitary; aggressive to others of the same species

**Breeding** Two to 4 young born April–May after gestation period of 31 days. Offspring spend a further 105 days in pouch. Weaned at 8 months; sexually mature at 2 years. May live up to 8 years in captivity, 6 in the wild

**Voice** Growls, grunts, barks, and screeches

**Diet** Mostly wallabies, wombats, sheep, and rabbits taken mainly as carrion

**Habitat** Heaths, forests, and other well-vegetated areas

**Distribution** Australian state of Tasmania

**Status** Population: abundant. Protected by Australian law; extinct in mainland Australia, but widespread and abundant in Tasmania

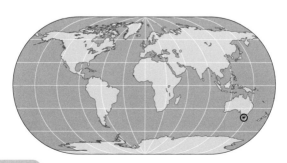

# Northern Quoll

**Common name** Northern quoll

**Scientific name** *Dasyurus hallucatus*

**Family** Dasyuridae

**Order** Dasyuromorphia

**Size** Length head/body: 5-12 in (13-30 cm); tail length: 5-12 in (13-30 cm); height at shoulder: 4-6 in (11-15 cm). Male larger than female

**Weight** 11-32 oz (300-900 g)

**Key features** Lithe-looking animal with long, thickly furred tail; small head with pointed snout; fur dark brown above, paler on underside; white spots on back; female has 6-8 teats covered by flap of skin when breeding

**Habits** Nocturnal; hunts in trees; solitary, territorial, and highly aggressive

**Breeding** One to 8 young born in July after 21 days' gestation. Young remain attached to teats for up to 2 months. Weaned at 3-5 months; sexually mature at 10-11 months. Probably lives for about 3 years in the wild

**Voice** Generally silent

**Diet** Small mammals, including rats; also reptiles, insects, worms, fruit, and honey

**Habitat** Wooded areas, usually within 90 miles (145 km) of the coast

**Distribution** Isolated populations in northern Australia, including parts of Western Australia, Northern Territories, and Queensland

**Status** Population: a few thousand; IUCN Lower Risk: near threatened. Has declined since European settlement; now protected

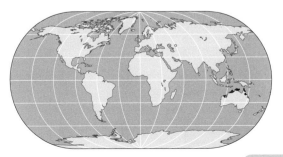

# Numbat

**Common name** Numbat (banded anteater, marsupial anteater)

**Scientific name** *Myrmecobius fasciatus*

**Family** Myrmecobiidae

**Order** Dasyuromorphia

**Size** Length head/body: 7–11 in (17–27 cm); tail length: 5–8 in (13–21 cm)

**Weight** 11–23 oz (300–650 g)

**Key features** Vaguely squirrel-like animal with long, tapering tail and large feet with long claws; fur gray, tinged red on upper back, paler beneath; rump distinctly marked with white bars; muzzle long and pointed with small, black nose and erect ears; eyes large with dark stripe running through each; female has 4 teats, but no pouch

**Habits** Solitary; active during the day; lively, nimble creature that climbs well

**Breeding** Two to 4 young born December–April after 14 days' gestation. Young carried attached to teats for 4 months. Weaned at 6 months; sexually mature from 9 months. May live at least 6 years in captivity, 6 in the wild

**Voice** Soft snuffling sounds; hisses when disturbed

**Diet** Mostly termites and ants; some other insects

**Habitat** Dry, open woodlands and semidesert scrub

**Distribution** Southwestern parts of Western Australia

**Status** Population: unknown, but declining; IUCN Vulnerable. Once found over much of southwestern and south-central Australia; now restricted to a few small areas in Western Australia; conservation has saved the species from extinction

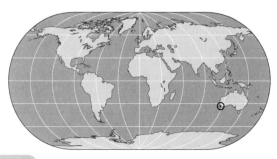

# Thylacine

**Common name** Thylacine (Tasmanian wolf, Tasmanian tiger)

**Scientific name** *Thylacinus cynocephalus*

**Family** Thylacinidae

**Order** Dasyuromorphia

**Size** Length head/body: 33–51 in (85–130 cm); tail length: 15–26 in (38–65 cm); height at shoulder: 14–24 in (35–60 cm)

**Weight** 33–66 lb (15–30 kg)

**Key features** Superficially doglike animal, with a long body and long, rather stiff tail; coat short and coarse; tawny brown with dark stripes across the back, rump, and base of tail; female has simple, crescent-shaped, rear-opening pouch

**Habits** Active at night; usually solitary, although may have hunted cooperatively

**Breeding** Two to 4 young born after gestation period of about 1 month. Carried in pouch for 3 months. Weaned at about 9 months; sexual maturity unknown. (NB: all estimates from captive animals, situation in wild unknown). Lived up to 13 years in captivity, unknown in the wild

**Voice** Whines, growls, barks, and sharp yaps

**Diet** Mammals, including kangaroos, wallabies, smaller marsupials, and rodents; also birds

**Habitat** Forests

**Distribution** Widespread in Australia and New Guinea until about 3,000 years ago; restricted to Tasmania in historical times, but now extinct

**Status** Population: 0; IUCN Extinct

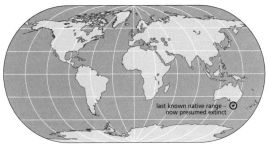

last known native range – now presumed extinct

231

# Common Dunnart

**Common name** Common dunnart (narrow-footed marsupial mouse)

**Scientific name** *Sminthopsis murina*

**Family** Dasyuridae

**Order** Dasyuromorphia

**Size** Length head/body: 2.5–4 in (6.5–10.5 cm); tail length: 3–4 in (7–10 cm)

**Weight** 0.35–1 oz (10–28 g)

**Key features** Mouselike marsupial with long, tapering snout and long, thin tail; fur brownish-gray above, white below; female has 8–10 teats in pouch

**Habits** Active at night; hunts on the ground or leaps into the air to intercept prey such as moths; usually solitary

**Breeding** Litters of up to 8 young born August–March after gestation period of 13 days. Incubated in pouch for 40–45 days. Weaned at 65 days; females sexually mature at about 4 months, males at 5–6 months. May live up to 4 years in captivity, rarely more than 2 in the wild

**Voice** Squeaks associated with courtship and aggression

**Diet** Insects and their larvae, especially beetles; also spiders; will scavenge human refuse

**Habitat** Woodland and heathland

**Distribution** Southeastern Australia (Victoria, New South Wales, southeastern South Australia) and north-eastern Queensland

**Status** Population: abundant. Common and widespread

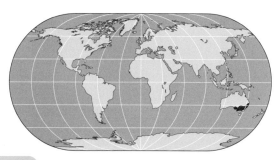

# Brown Antechinus

**Common name** Brown antechinus

**Scientific name** *Antechinus stuartii*

**Family** Dasyuridae

**Order** Dasyuromorphia

**Size** Length head/body: 3–5.5 in (7–14 cm); tail length: 2–4 in (6–11 cm)

**Weight** 1–2.5 oz (28–70 g)

**Key features** Mouselike animal; pointed nose; large ears; long, hairy tail; coat short, tawny to fawn, paler underneath; feet broad with 5 toes on each; 1st toe is small and lacks claw; female has 6–10 teats, but no pouch

**Habits** Active at night, usually terrestrial, but can climb well; males especially gregarious

**Breeding** Six to 12 young born in October after gestation period of 27 days. Weaned at 3 months; sexually mature at 9 months. Females may live 2 years, males 11 months in the wild, not usually kept in captivity

**Voice** Sharp squeaks by males during aggressive encounters

**Diet** Insects, especially beetles; also spiders, crustaceans, and other invertebrates

**Habitat** Forest; also areas of scrub

**Distribution** Eastern Australia: main population lives along coast of New South Wales and southern Queensland; second, smaller population farther north around Cairns

**Status** Population: abundant. Common where it occurs

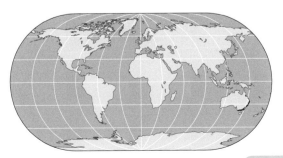

# Marsupial Mole

**Common name** Marsupial mole

**Scientific name** *Notoryctes typhlops*

**Family** Notoryctidae

**Order** Notoryctemorphia

**Size** Length head/body: 4–6 in (10–16 cm); tail length: 1 in (2.5 cm)

**Weight** 1.2–2.5 oz (34–70 g)

**Key features** Flat-bodied animal with pale golden fur and very short legs; front feet spadelike; no functional eyes; ear holes hidden in fur; nose has tough shield; tail is short and stubby; female has 2 teats in rear-opening pouch

**Habits** Solitary; "swims" through sand without creating permanent tunnels

**Breeding** Details not known

**Voice** Not known, but probably silent

**Diet** Insect grubs and other soil invertebrates; captive individuals are known to eat small reptiles

**Habitat** Desert

**Distribution** Central and northwestern Australia

**Status** Population: unknown; IUCN Endangered. Feared to be in decline

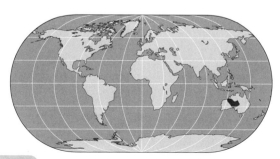

# Bilby

**Common name**
Bilby (greater bilby, rabbit-eared bandicoot)

**Scientific name** *Macrotis lagotis*

**Family** Peramelidae

**Order** Peramelemorphia

**Size** Length head/body: 12–14 in (30–55 cm); tail length: 8–11.5 in (20–29 cm)

**Weight** 1.8–5.5 lb (0.8–2.5 kg)

**Key features** Rabbit-sized animal; slender legs; long, furry tail; pointed nose; huge rabbitlike ears; silky fur gray above, white below; 1st half of tail black, while rest is white to the tip; female has 8 teats in backward-opening pouch

**Habits** Active at night; terrestrial, lives in burrows; generally solitary, but not territorial

**Breeding** One to 2 young (occasionally 3) born at any time of year after gestation period of 14 days. Incubated in pouch for 80 days. Weaned at 95 days; females sexually mature at 5–7 months, males at 9–13 months. May live up to 7 years in captivity, fewer in the wild

**Voice** Virtually silent, except for snuffling noises; may huff when threatened

**Diet** Mostly insects and other invertebrates; also some small vertebrate animals and plant material

**Habitat** Dry woodland, scrub, and grassland

**Distribution** Central Australia

**Status** Population: maybe low thousands; IUCN Vulnerable; CITES I. Range and population have declined greatly in recent times

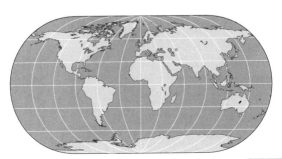

# Northern Bandicoot

**Common name** Northern bandicoot (northern brown bandicoot, large short-nosed bandicoot)

**Scientific name** *Isoodon macrourus*

**Family** Peramelidae

**Order** Peramelemorphia

**Size** Length head/body: 12–18.5 in (30–47 cm); tail length: 3–8 in (8–21 cm)

**Weight** 1.1–6.7 lb (0.5–3 kg)

**Key features** Rabbit-sized, ratlike animal with a long, pointed face, glossy brown fur, long, hairy tail, and very long claws; female has 8 teats in rear-opening pouch

**Habits** Nocturnal; active on the ground; a solitary and aggressive creature

**Breeding** One to 7 (usually 3 or 4) young born at any time of year after gestation period of just 12.5 days. Incubated in pouch for 60 days. Weaned at 8–10 weeks; sexually mature at 4 months. May live up to 4 years in the wild, not usually kept in captivity

**Voice** Generally silent

**Diet** Insects, worms, and other invertebrates; also some fruit, seeds, and nonleafy plant material

**Habitat** Open woodland and dense scrub, especially close to rivers and swamps

**Distribution** Northern and eastern coasts of Australia, New Guinea, and nearby islands

**Status** Population: abundant. Common within its geographical range

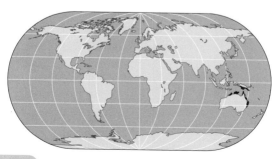

# Red Kangaroo

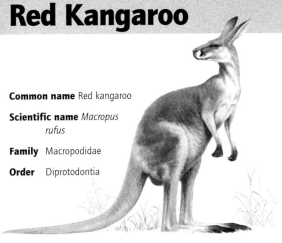

**Common name** Red kangaroo

**Scientific name** *Macropus rufus*

**Family** Macropodidae

**Order** Diprotodontia

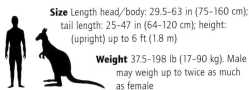

**Size** Length head/body: 29.5–63 in (75–160 cm); tail length: 25–47 in (64–120 cm); height: (upright) up to 6 ft (1.8 m)

**Weight** 37.5–198 lb (17–90 kg). Male may weigh up to twice as much as female

**Key features** Large kangaroo with rusty-red to blue-gray fur, paler on belly; female has 4 teats in a well-developed, forward-facing pouch

**Habits** Lives in loose groups; most active between dusk and dawn

**Breeding** Single young born at any time of year after gestation period of 33 days (plus up to 6 months delayed implantation). Incubated in pouch for 235 days. Weaned at 12 months; females sexually mature at 15–20 months, males at 20–24 months. May live more than 30 years in captivity, 27 in the wild

**Voice** Gruff coughing sounds

**Diet** Mainly grass; also leaves of other plants, including shrubs and trees

**Habitat** Scrub and open grassland, including arid and semiarid areas

**Distribution** Throughout central Australia; absent from the far north, eastern, and southeastern coasts, southwestern Australia, and Tasmania

**Status** Population: abundant. Remains common and widespread despite hunting and other control measures

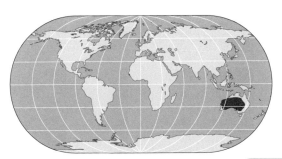

# Gray Kangaroo

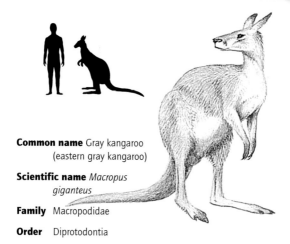

**Common name** Gray kangaroo (eastern gray kangaroo)

**Scientific name** *Macropus giganteus*

**Family** Macropodidae

**Order** Diprotodontia

**Size** Length head/body: 33–55 in (85–140 cm); tail length: 29.5–39 in (75–100 cm); height at shoulder: up to 6 ft (1.8 m). Male substantially larger than female

**Weight** 44–145 lb (20–66 kg)

**Key features** Large, muscular kangaroo with coarse silvery gray fur, paler on belly; often feet, tail, and face much darker; face furrier than in red kangaroo; female has 4 teats in well-developed, forward-opening pouch

**Habits** Mostly nocturnal; often lives in large groups; agile on open ground

**Breeding** Single young born at any time of year after gestation period of 36 days (plus up to 7 months delayed implantation). Incubated in pouch for 11 months. Weaned at 18 months; females sexually mature at 20–36 months, males at 20–72 months. May live up to 24 years in captivity, 20 in the wild

**Voice** Gruff cough when alarmed or annoyed

**Diet** Grass and other plant material

**Habitat** Scrub, woodland, and forest in areas with more than 10 in (250 mm) annual rainfall

**Distribution** Eastern Australia (most of Queensland, New South Wales, and Victoria); also extreme southeastern part of South Australia and northeastern part of Tasmania

**Status** Population: abundant. Common and widespread; hunted under license

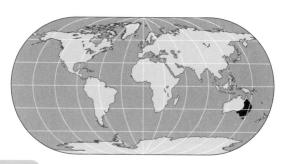

# Red-Necked Wallaby

**Common name** Red-necked wallaby (Bennett's wallaby)

**Scientific name** *Macropus rufogriseus*

**Family** Macropodidae

**Order** Diprotodontia

**Size** Length head/body: 26–35 in (66–89 cm); tail length: 24–34 in (62–87 cm); height at shoulder: about 30 in (75 cm). Male larger than female

**Weight** 24–60 lb (11–27 kg)

**Key features** Medium-sized kangaroo with light-brown or grayish fur, reddish on nape of neck and shoulders; female has 4 teats in forward-opening pouch

**Habits** Generally nocturnal; lives alone or in small groups

**Breeding** One (occasionally 2 or 3) young born at any time of year after gestation period of 30 days (plus up to 11 months delayed implantation). Leaves pouch after 280 days. Weaned at 1 year; females sexually mature at 14 months, males at 19 months. May live over 20 years in captivity, 18 in the wild

**Voice** Occasional soft grunts

**Diet** Grass and other plant material

**Habitat** Various kinds of eucalyptus forest

**Distribution** Southeastern Australia, including Tasmania; introduced to New Zealand and Britain

**Status** Population: abundant. Common and numerous in most parts of its range; hunted for skins and as a pest in Tasmania

# Quokka

**Common name** Quokka

**Scientific name** *Setonix brachyurus*

**Family**  Macropodidae

**Order**  Diprotodontia

**Size**  Length head/body: 19–24 in (48–60 cm);
tail length: 10–14 in (25–35 cm)

**Weight** 4.5–11 lb (2–5 kg)

**Key features** Small, grayish-brown furred wallaby with a short,
sparsely furred tail; short, furry face with small, round
ears; hind feet larger than front feet; female has 4 teats
inside a well-developed, forward-facing pouch

**Habits**  Nocturnal; normally ground dwelling, but can climb;
often lives in groups

**Voice**  Generally silent

**Breeding** Single young born at any time of year (seasonal in
island populations) after gestation period of 27 days
(plus up to 5 months delayed implantation). Leaves
pouch at 6 months. Weaned at 9–10 months; females
sexually mature at 8–9 months, males at about 14
months. May live at least 7 years in captivity, 10
in the wild

**Diet**  Mostly leaves and shoots

**Habitat** Areas of dense, swampy vegetation in forests; also dry,
open terrain

**Distribution** Localized populations in southwestern Australia;
also on Rottnest and Bald Islands off Western Australia

**Status**  Population: about 2,500; IUCN Vulnerable. Has
undergone a serious decline

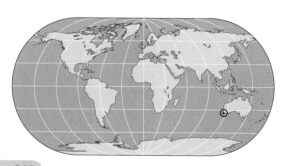

# Potoroo

**Common name** Potoroo (long-nosed potoroo)

**Scientific name** *Potorous tridactylus*

**Family** Potoridae

**Order** Diprotodontia

**Size** Length head/body: 13–15 in (34–38 cm); tail length: 8–10 in (20–26 cm)

**Weight** 1.5–3.6 lb (0.6–1.6 kg)

**Key features** Compact, short-haired animal with thick, hairy tail; gray-brown fur, paler underneath; hind feet long with well-muscled legs; conical face with small nose, round ears, and large, black eyes; female has 4 teats in forward-opening pouch

**Habits** Shy; active at night; solitary; digs for food

**Breeding** Two litters per year, each of 1 young, born after gestation period of 4.5 months (including delayed implantation). Leaves pouch at 130 days. Weaned at about 5 months; sexually mature at 1 year. May live up to 12 years in captivity, 7 in the wild

**Voice** Generally silent

**Diet** Roots, shoots, tubers, fungi, insects, other invertebrates

**Habitat** Coastal heaths and forest with dense ground cover in areas of high rainfall

**Distribution** Southeastern coasts of Australia, including Tasmania, Victoria, and New South Wales; also extreme southern corners of South Australia, Queensland, and Western Australia

**Status** Population: fewer than 10,000; IUCN Vulnerable. In decline since European settlement; now protected

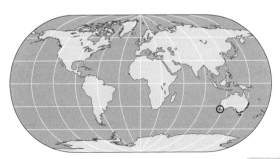

# Common Brushtail Possum

**Common name** Common brushtail possum

**Scientific name** *Trichosurus vulpecula*

**Family** Phalangeridae

**Order** Diprotodontia

**Size** Length head/body: 14–22 in (35–55 cm); tail length: 10–16 in (25–40 cm). Male grows bigger than female

**Weight** 2.5–10 lb (1–4.5 kg)

**Key features** Large possum; oval ears; big brown eyes; fur grayish-brown; male often more reddish; long, furry tail is naked just under tip; large feet with 5 well-developed claws; 2nd and 3rd toes of hind feet are joined; female has 2 teats in well-developed, forward-opening pouch

**Habits** Active at night; largely arboreal; solitary; sometimes territorial; often found near human habitation

**Breeding** Single young (occasionally twins) born after gestation period of 17 days. Leaves pouch at 4 months. Weaned at 6 months; sexually mature at 9–12 months. May live up to 15 years in captivity, 13 in the wild

**Voice** Huffing, grunting, and clicking sounds; also loud screams when angry

**Diet** Mostly plants, including leaves, grass, seeds, flowers, and fruit; also insects, young birds, and eggs; human refuse

**Habitat** Forests; cities and towns

**Distribution** Australia; introduced to New Zealand

**Status** Population: abundant. Common and widespread; considered a pest in New Zealand

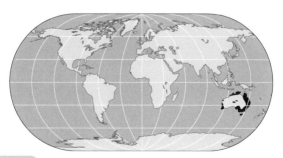

# Spotted Cuscus

**Common name** Spotted cuscus (common spotted cuscus)

**Scientific name** *Spilocuscus maculatus*

**Family** Phalangeridae

**Order** Diprotodontia

**Size** Length head/body: 14–23 in (35–58 cm); tail length: 12–17 in (30–43.5 cm)

**Weight** 3.3–11 lb (1.5–5 kg)

**Key features** Large, long-tailed, woolly-looking possum with round head, small ears, and huge, round eyes; usually pale creamy-white with dark "saddle," often gray blotches (in males) or pale-gray body with pale patches in females; female has 4 teats in pouch

**Habits** Solitary; nocturnal; arboreal

**Breeding** Little known. One to 3 young probably born at any time throughout the year. Gestation, weaning, and sexual maturity unknown. May live up to 11 years in captivity, unknown in the wild

**Voice** Hisses, screeches, and clicks; females especially noisy when in breeding condition

**Diet** Mostly fruit (such as figs), flowers, and leaves; probably also eats insects and other small animals it comes across

**Habitat** Rain forest; also open woodland and mangroves

**Distribution** New Guinea and surrounding islands; also Cape York area in northeastern Australia

**Status** Population: abundant

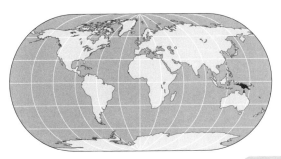

# Sugar Glider

**Common name** Sugar glider

**Scientific name** *Petaurus breviceps*

**Family** Petauridae

**Order** Diprotodontia

**Size** Length head/body: 6–8 in (15–21 cm); tail length: 6.5–8 in (16.5–21 cm). Male larger than female

**Weight** 2.8–4.8 oz (80–135 g)

**Key features** Small possum with long, furry tail and furry gliding membrane from wrist to ankle on either side of body; fur soft and pale gray with darker markings on face; dark stripe down back and on tail tip, paler on belly; female has 4 teats in well-developed pouch

**Habits** Social, but territorial; active at night; excellent climber and glider; bold and curious

**Breeding** Two young born June–July after gestation period of 16 days. Spend 70 days in pouch and a further 50 in communal nest. Weaned at about 3 months; sexually mature at 12 months. May live up to 9 years, usually fewer

**Voice** Grumbles, chatters, shrieks, screams, and high-pitched yapping sounds, mostly when angry, frightened, or disturbed

**Diet** Varied; includes plant sap and gum, pollen, nectar, fruit, honey, and seeds; also insects, spiders, and other invertebrates

**Habitat** Varied; anywhere with suitable food and nesting sites such as hollow trees or nest boxes; especially forests and wooded areas; tolerant of disturbance

**Distribution** Northern, eastern, and southeastern Australia, including Tasmania; also on New Guinea and many smaller Australasian islands

**Status** Population: abundant. Common and widespread within its range

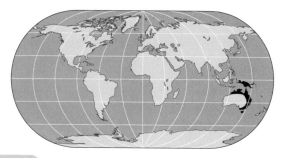

# Leadbeater's Possum

**Common name** Leadbeater's possum

**Scientific name** *Gymnobelideus leadbeateri*

**Family** Petauridae

**Order** Diprotodontia

**Size** Length head/body: about 6 in (15 cm); tail length: 6 in (15 cm)

**Weight** 2.5–6 oz (70–170 g)

**Key features** Typical small possum with long, furry tail and large ears; velvety-gray fur marked with dark stripe down back; eyes very large and black; female has front-opening pouch

**Habits** Nocturnal; arboreal; territorial; lives in loose social groups dominated by females

**Breeding** One or 2 young born at any time of year except midsummer after gestation period of 15–17 days. Leaves pouch at 90 days. Weaned at 3 months; sexually mature at 2 years. May live up to 9 years in captivity, 7 in the wild

**Voice** Chattering calls and angry hisses

**Diet** Mostly insects; some sap, gum, and honeydew

**Habitat** Australian mountain ash forests where there is dense wattle acacia undergrowth

**Distribution** Central highlands of Victoria, Australia

**Status** Population: fewer than 5,000; IUCN Endangered. Previously thought to be extinct

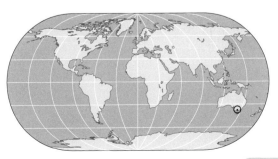

# Copper Ringtail

**Common name** Copper ringtail

**Scientific name** *Pseudochirops cupreus*

**Family** Pseudocheiridae

**Order** Diprotodontia

**Size** Length head/body: 14–16 in (35–41 cm); tail length: 10–12 in (26–31 cm)

**Weight** 3–5 lb (1.4–2.3 kg)

**Key features** Possum with dense, woolly fur that has a coppery sheen; about half the tail is naked and usually held partially curled

**Habits** Nocturnal; arboreal; normally solitary

**Breeding** Little known for certain. Probably only 1 young born at a time at any time of year. Gestation, weaning, sexual maturity, and life span unknown

**Voice** Probably silent most of the time

**Diet** Generally leaves; also perhaps some fruit

**Habitat** Mountain forest, mostly above 6,000 ft (2,000 m)

**Distribution** Central highlands of New Guinea

**Status** Population: abundant. Localized distribution, but apparently plentiful where it occurs

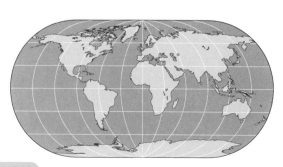

# Koala

**Common name** Koala (koala bear, native Australian bear)

**Scientific name** *Phascolarctos cinereus*

**Family** Phascolarctidae

**Order** Diprotodontia

**Size** Length head/body: 24–33 in (60–85 cm). Male larger than female; southern koalas larger than northern ones

**Weight** 9–33 lb (4–15 kg)

**Key features** Compact and teddy-bearlike with woolly, grayish-brown fur, paler on belly; large head with round, fluffy ears and large, black nose; tail stumpy; legs longer than they first appear, with 5 large claws on each foot; female has 2 teats in backward-opening pouch

**Habits** Solitary; nocturnal; arboreal; may come to the ground to cross open spaces

**Breeding** Single young (occasionally twins) born September to April (summer) after gestation period of 25–30 days. Leaves pouch after 5–7 months. Weaned at 6–12 months; sexually mature at 2 years. May live up to 20 years in captivity, 18 in the wild

**Voice** Screams, wheezing bellows, and loud wailing associated with courtship and aggression

**Diet** Leaves and bark of various species of eucalyptus trees

**Habitat** Eucalyptus forest and scrub

**Distribution** Eastern Australia

**Status** Population: about 40,000; IUCN Lower Risk: near threatened. Previously hunted for fur and threatened by loss of habitat; now protected and increasing

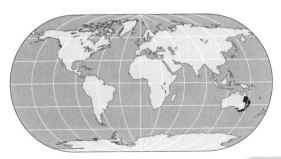

# Common Wombat

**Common name** Common wombat

**Scientific name** *Vombatus ursinus*

**Family**  Vombatidae

**Order**  Diprotodontia

**Size**  Length head/body: 27.5–47 in (70–120 cm); tail length: 1 in (2.5 cm)

**Weight**  33–77 lb (15–35 kg)

**Key features** Solid, short-legged, bearlike animal with very short tail; large head with short snout, large nose, and small ears; coat of coarse brown fur; long, powerful claws; female has 2 teats in rear-opening pouch

**Habits**  Solitary; mostly active at night; digs large burrows

**Breeding** Single young (occasionally twins) mostly born in summer or fall after gestation period of 21 days. Spends a further 2–3 months in pouch. Weaned at 15 months; sexually mature at 2 years. May live up to 26 years in captivity, but fewer in the wild

**Voice**  Grunts and abrupt coughing sounds

**Diet**  Plant material, including leaves, stems, and roots; also fungi

**Habitat** Forests and scrub in rocky upland areas

**Distribution** Southeastern Australia and Tasmania

**Status**  Population: many thousands; IUCN Vulnerable (Flinders Island subspecies). Has declined, but remains secure and common in parts of its geographical range away from human habitation

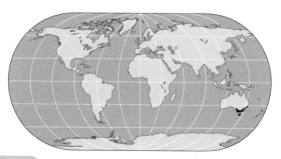

# Honey Possum

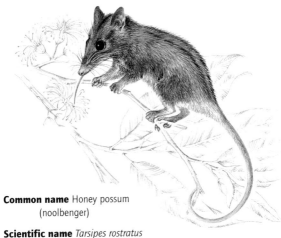

**Common name** Honey possum (noolbenger)

**Scientific name** *Tarsipes rostratus*

**Family** Tarsipedidae

**Order** Diprotodontia

**Size** Length head/body: 1.5–4 in (4–9.5 cm); tail length: 2–4 in (4.5–11 cm)

**Weight** 0.2–0.6 oz (7–16 g)

**Key features** Tiny, mouselike marsupial with gray-brown fur marked with 3 dark stripes along the back; long snout and very long tail with hooked, prehensile tip; fingers are long with large, rounded tips and small nails; female has 4 teats in well-developed pouch

**Habits** Nocturnal; arboreal; excellent climber; often gregarious (lives in groups); goes torpid in cold weather

**Breeding** Two to 3 young born at any time of year after gestation period of 21–28 days (plus up to 2 months delayed development in the womb). Leaves pouch at about 4–6 weeks. Weaned at 10 weeks; sexually mature at 10 months. Rarely lives more than 1 year

**Voice** Normally silent

**Diet** Pollen and nectar

**Habitat** Trees and shrubs

**Distribution** Southwestern parts of Western Australia

**Status** Population: unknown but common. Not currently threatened, but may be at risk from habitat loss

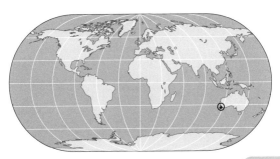

# Duck-Billed Platypus

**Common name** Duck-billed platypus

**Scientific name** *Ornithorhynchus anatinus*

**Family** Ornithorhynchidae

**Order** Monotremata

**Size** Length head/body: 12–18 in (30–45 cm); tail length: 4–6 in (10–15 cm). Male usually larger than female

**Weight** 1–4.4 lb (0.5–2 kg)

**Key features** Flattened, torpedo-shaped animal with very short legs and large feet, each with 5 webbed toes; snout has soft, rubbery beak with nostrils on top; tail flat and paddlelike; body fur dark brown on back, paler below; male has sharp spurs on ankles

**Habits** Largely aquatic; most active around dusk and dawn; lives in burrows; generally solitary

**Breeding** One to 3 (usually 2) eggs laid after gestation period of 27 days. Young hatch 10 days later and are brooded for a further 4 months in nest burrow. Weaned at 4 months; sexually mature at 2 or 3 years. May live up to 21 years in captivity, 14 in the wild

**Voice** Usually silent; growls if disturbed or annoyed

**Diet** Small aquatic animals, especially crustaceans, insect larvae, worms, fish, and tadpoles

**Habitat** Freshwater streams and pools with suitable burrowing sites along their banks

**Distribution** Eastern Australia, including parts of Tasmania, New South Wales, Victoria, South Australia, and Queensland

**Status** Population: low thousands. Previously hunted for fur, now protected and doing well in most of its range

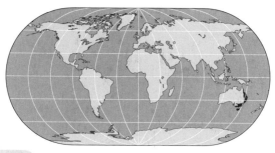

# Short-Beaked Echidna

**Common name** Short-beaked echidna (short-nosed spiny anteater)

**Scientific name** *Tachyglossus aculeatus*

**Family** Tachyglossidae

**Order** Monotremata

**Size** Length head/body: 14–21 in (35–53 cm); tail length: 3.5 in (9 cm)

**Weight** 5.5–15.5 lb (2.5–7 kg)

**Key features** Stocky, short-legged animal with domed back covered in thick, dark-brown fur and long, black-tipped yellow spines; large feet have 5 toes with large, blunt claws; tail short; head small with long, whiskerless snout

**Habits** Solitary, but nonterritorial; usually nocturnal; may hibernate in parts of its range; terrestrial, but swims and climbs well; powerful digger

**Breeding** Single egg laid July–August after gestation period of 9–27 days. Incubated in pouchlike fold of skin on mother's belly; hatches after 10 days; spends further 8 weeks in pouch. Weaned at 6–7 months; sexually mature at 1–2 years. May live for over 50 years in captivity, rarely more than 20 in the wild

**Voice** Generally silent

**Diet** Ants and termites

**Habitat** Varied; forest and scrub, open rocky and sandy landscapes; also parks and gardens

**Distribution** Australia, including Tasmania; also New Guinea

**Status** Population: abundant. Common and widespread

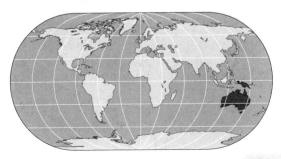

# Glossary

Words in SMALL CAPITALS refer to other entries in the glossary.

**Antler** branched prongs on head of male deer, made of solid bone

**Aquatic** living in water

**Arboreal** living among the branches of trees

**Baleen** horny substance commonly known as whalebone and growing as plates in the mouth of certain whales; used like a sieve to extract plankton from seawater

**Boreal forests** Arctic forests (mostly conifers) at high latitudes

**Breeding season** the entire cycle of reproductive activity from courtship, pair formation (and often establishment of TERRITORY), through nesting to independence of young

**Browsing** feeding on leaves of trees and shrubs

**Canopy** continuous (closed canopy) or broken (open canopy) layer in forests produced by the intermingling of branches

**Carnivore** meat-eating animal

**Carrion** dead animal matter used as a food source by SCAVENGERS

**CITES** Convention on International Trade in Endangered Species. Restricts international trade by licensing controls. Rare animals and plants listed in Appendices: I—endangered and most restricted trade; II—not endangered but could be if trade not restricted; III—least restricted trade

**Coniferous forest** evergreen forest of northern regions and mountainous areas dominated by pines, spruces, and cedars

**Crepuscular** active in twilight

**Delayed implantation** when the development of a fertilized egg is suspended for a variable period before it implants into the wall of the uterus and completes normal pregnancy. Births are thus delayed until a favorable time of year

**Den** a shelter, natural or constructed, used for sleeping, giving birth, and raising young

**Display** any relatively conspicuous pattern of behavior that conveys specific information to others, usually members of the same SPECIES; can involve visual or vocal elements, as in threat, courtship, or greeting displays

**Diurnal** active during the day

**Dorsal** relating to the back or spinal part of the body; usually the upper surface

**Echolocation** the process of perception based on reaction to the pattern of reflected sound waves (echos)

**Estivation** a period of inactivity or greatly decreased activity during hot or dry weather

**Family** technical term for group of closely related SPECIES that often also look similar. Zoological family names always end in "idae" Also, a social group within a species consisting of parents and their offspring

**Feral** domestic animals that have gone wild

**Flippers** flattened front limbs of sea mammals used for steering underwater and (in the case of fur seals, walrus, and sea lions) for locomotion on land

**Flukes** flattened tail fins of whales

**Forage** to search for food, usually by BROWSING or GRAZING

**Forb** a herb other than grass

**Generalist** an animal that is capable of a wide range of activities, not specialized

**Genus** a group of closely related SPECIES. The plural is genera

**Gestation** the period of pregnancy between fertilization of the egg and birth of the baby

**Grazing** feeding on grass

**Gregarious** living together in loose groups or herds

**Guard hairs** long, shiny hairs that project from UNDERFUR, particularly prominent in some AQUATIC rodents and CARNIVORES

**Harem** a group of females living in the same TERRITORY and consorting with a single male

**Herbivore** plant-eating animal

**Hibernation** a period of inactivity in winter, with lowered body temperature to save energy

**Home range** the area that an animal uses in the course of its normal periods of activity

**Incubation** the act of incubating eggs, i.e. keeping them warm, so that development is possible

**Insectivores** animals that feed on insects and similar small prey. Also a group name for animals such as hedgehogs, shrews, and moles

**Invertebrates** animals that have no backbone (or other true bones) inside their body, e.g., mollusks, insects, jellyfish, and crabs

**IUCN** International Union for the Conservation of Nature, responsible for assigning animals and plants to internationally agreed categories of rarity. (See table below)

**Juvenile** young animal that has not yet reached breeding age

**Mammae** See MAMMARY GLANDS

**Mammary glands** characteristic of mammals, glands for production of milk

**Mangroves** woody shrubs and trees adapted to living along muddy coasts in the tropics

**Migration** movement from one place to another and back again, usually seasonal

**Molt** process in which mammals shed hair, usually seasonal

**Monogamous** animals that have only one mate at a time

Monotreme egg-laying mammal, e.g., platypus, echidna

**Montane** in a mountain environment

**Musk** a substance with a penetrating odor produced in a sac beneath the abdominal skin of certain animals

**Muzzle** the projecting jaws and nose of an animal; snout

**Nocturnal** active at night

**Nomadic** animals that have no fixed home, but wander continuously

**Nose-leaf** fleshy structures around the face of bats; help focus ULTRASOUNDS used for ECHOLOCATION

**Omnivore** an animal that eats almost anything, meat or vegetable

**Opportunistic** taking advantage of every varied opportunity that arises; flexible behavior

**Opposable** fingers or toes that can be brought to bear against others on the same hand or foot in order to grip objects

**Order** a subdivision of a class of animals consisting of a series of related animal FAMILIES

**Pair bond** behavior that keeps a male and a female together beyond the time it takes to mate

**Parasite** animal or plant that lives on or in body of another

**Population** a distinct group of animals of the same SPECIES or all the animals of that species

**Precocious** when offspring develop early for their age

**Predator** an animal that kills live prey for food

**Prehensile** grasping tail or fingers

**Pride** SOCIAL group of lions

**Primate** a group of mammals that includes monkeys, apes, and humans

**Promiscuous** mating often with many mates, not just one

**Pup** name given to a young seal or sea lion

**Range** the total geographical area over which a SPECIES is distributed

**Retractile** capable of being withdrawn, as in the claws of typical cats, which can be folded back into the paws to protect from damage when walking

**Riparian** living beside rivers and lakes

**Roost** place that a bat or a bird regularly uses for sleeping

**Ruminant** animals that eat vegetation and later bring it back from the stomach to chew again ("chewing the cud" or "rumination") to assist its digestion by microbes in the stomach

**Rut** annually recurring state of sexual excitement in male deer (and other mammals); also used to describe the period during which this occurs

**Savanna** tropical grasslands with scattered trees and low rainfall, usually in warm areas

**Scavenger** animal that feeds on dead animals or plants that it has not hunted or collected itself

**Scrotum** bag of skin within which the male testicles are located

**Scrub** vegetation that is dominated by shrubs—woody plants usually with more than one stem

**Secondary forest** trees that have been planted or grown up on cleared ground

**Sexually mature** having reached full reproductive development

**Social** living together in colonies

**Solitary** living alone or undertaking tasks alone

**Species** a group of animals that look similar and can breed to produce fertile offspring

**Spy-hopping** when a whale raises its head vertically out of the water to look around

**Steppe** open grassland in parts of the world where the climate is too harsh for trees to grow

**Sub-Saharan** all parts of Africa lying south of the Sahara Desert

**Subspecies** a locally distinct group of animals that differ slightly from normal appearance of SPECIES; often called a race

**Temperate** associated with a moderate climate

**Terrestrial** living on land

**Territory** an area that one or more animals defend against other members of the same SPECIES; these animals are territorial

**Tragus** fleshy lobe at the base of a mammal's ear, important for identifying bat SPECIES

**Tropics** permanently warm zone of the earth's surface centered on the equator, lying between the Tropic of Capricorn and Tropic of Cancer

**Tundra** open grassy or shrub-covered lands of the far north

**Ultrasounds** sounds that are too high-pitched for humans to hear

**Underfur** fine hairs forming a dense, woolly mass close to the skin and underneath the outer coat of stiff hairs in mammals

**Ungulate** hoofed animals such as pigs, deer, cattle, and horses; mostly HERBIVORES

**Weaned** able to take food other than by nursing from the mother

## IUCN CATEGORIES

**EX** **Extinct**, when there is no reasonable doubt that the last individual of the species has died.

**EW** **Extinct in the Wild**, when a species is known only to survive in captivity or as a naturalized population well outside the past range.

**CR** **Critically Endangered**, when a species is facing an extremely high risk of extinction in the wild in the immediate future.

**EN** **Endangered**, when a species is facing a very high risk of extinction in the wild in the near future.

**VU** **Vulnerable**, when a species is facing a high risk of extinction in the wild in the medium-term future.

**LR** **Lower Risk**, when a species has been evaluated and does not satisfy the criteria for CR, EN, or VU.

**DD** **Data Deficient**, when there is not enough information about a species to assess the risk of extinction.

**NE** **Not Evaluated**, species that have not been assessed by the IUCN criteria.

# Index

**255**